The Celebrated Cases of Dick Tracy

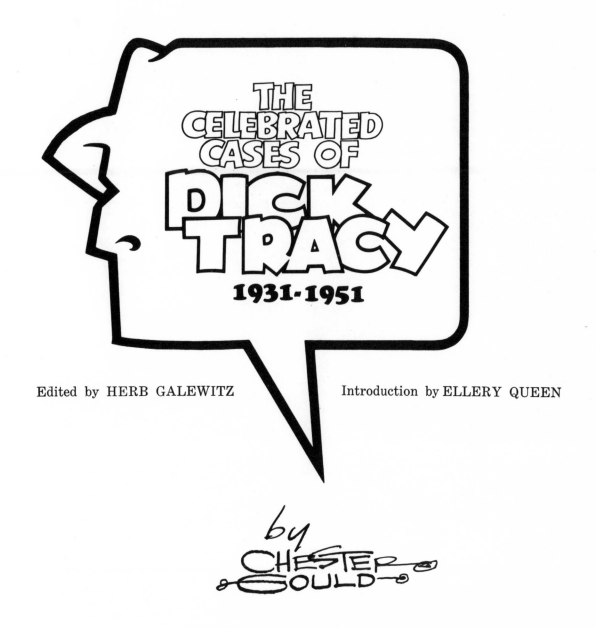

THE CELEBRATED CASES OF DICK TRACY

1931-1951

Edited by HERB GALEWITZ   Introduction by ELLERY QUEEN

by CHESTER GOULD

Chelsea House   New York

We wish to thank Henry Raduta and the staff of the
Chicago Tribune–New York News Syndicate, Inc. for their
considerable help in the preparation of this volume.

Library of Congress Catalog Card Number: 70-127010
Standard Book Number: 394-41964-Z
Distributed by Random House, Inc.

Manufactured in the United States of America

First Edition

CONTENTS

Interview with Chester Gould

Q: What can you tell us about your early days?

Gould: I was born in Oklahoma and my grandfather on my mother's side was one of the men that made the trek into Oklahoma to stake out a claim. His name was Riley Miller. He took his family there in 1892 and built a log cabin which is still standing. It's not very sturdy but it's there. On my father's side, my grandfather Gould was a minister who moved west from West Virginia. My own father was a printer and eventually the owner of a weekly newspaper. It was probably that influence which got me into the frame of mind to become a cartoonist.

I remember very well one time when I was seven. My dad was then editing a weekly newspaper and there was to be a Pawnee County, Oklahoma political meeting. He said, "Would you like to draw some of the men at this meeting?" Well, you can imagine how good my efforts must have been at that age. But I went over and turned out a bunch of stuff; they pasted it up in the window of the Pawnee *Courier Dispatch,* which was located right next to the post office. Everybody walked to the post office for the mail, so they had to pass my drawings. I got considerable attention and I think it's perhaps the thing that definitely turned me into this business. I have been at it since 1907.

Q: What were some of your favorite cartoons in those days?

Gould: Head and shoulders above everything else was "Mutt and Jeff." It was brand new and my father used to buy the Oklahoma City *Daily Oklahoman* just so that I could read "Mutt and Jeff." "Buster Brown" was big then too. So was "Little Nemo," and "Slim Jim."

Q: Did you finish your schooling in Oklahoma?

Gould: I went to Oklahoma A&M College for two years, and then moved on to Chicago in 1921 and finished up a four-year course in commerce and marketing at Northwestern University. I went to night school in the Loop and supported myself drawing cartoons and doing commercial work. Up to the time I started "Dick Tracy" in '31 I had worked on every paper in Chicago except the *Evening Post,* which went bankrupt or I probably would have ended up working on that too. However, I came to Chicago with the intent of getting on the *Tribune.* That was my goal.

Q: When you started Tracy, did you feel that it was a story about the times or was it just a good story line?

Gould: What was taking place then was the last stage, you might say, of big-time gangsterism in Chicago. I had submitted numerous ideas to the *Tribune* and to Captain Joe Patterson of the *Tribune* syndicate from 1921 until 1931 on various subjects. I found that none of them quite clicked. Then it suddenly dawned on me that perhaps we ought to have a detective in this country that would hunt these fellows up and shoot 'em down. So I developed this character called "Plainclothes Tracy."

Q: When you submitted the Tracy idea to Patterson, what was his reaction?

Gould: The Captain wired me from New York saying that he liked the idea and that I should get started on it. Only he said the name was too long and suggested I change it to "Dick Tracy." In fact, I owe everything that came to me in those days to the faith that J. M. Patterson had in this strip.

Q: Did Patterson contribute other ideas to the strip?

Gould: Yes, for the first year he came about once a month to contact cartoonists who were in Chicago and ask about their progress on their latest strips. After talking with us he would invariably have something to contribute—a story outline, a finale to a plot. He had a fantastic mind. He could talk to five cartoonists and give everyone of them a terrific idea.

Q: But you did have a few strips published prior to "Dick Tracy?"

Gould: Yes, for five years I did a strip for Hearst's *American*. It was a burlesque on the movies called "Fillum Fables," but I cannot claim originality for it. We already had a very capable man doing a strip like that—"Minute Movies" by Ed Wheelan.

Q: Wasn't that an era when newspapers really realized how important the cartoonists were in selling the papers.

Gould: That's true. And it is also true today. I believe that the biggest pulling magnet of newspapers today are comic strips.

Q: What was the immediate reaction of the public to your strip?

Gould: Like all things new, it took a couple of months to catch on. Then it grew like wildfire. The salesmen would call me up and say, "We got two new orders this morning." There would be two or three orders a day for many, many days. However, from the very beginning I would receive letters saying what a "horrible" strip I was doing.

Q: From individuals or organizations?

Gould: Mostly from individuals. Now I am used to it and take it with a grain of salt. They don't annoy me one whit any more. The odd thing about them, however, is that they would often describe in detail the "horrible things." I figured that they were the types who couldn't wait until the next day to see how a particular thing turned out.

Q: What about the reaction of police departments? Did they feel that Tracy was providing a good image?

Gould: I have in my home no less than a dozen citations and awards from police departments. I also had the privilege of spending some time with J. Edgar Hoover in the mid-30's.

Q: Do people today ever acknowledge that Dick Tracy influenced them in their youth?

Gould: Yes, I run into that very often, and I think that we all build our lives around heroes. I don't care how sophisticated you are, you want to be like somebody you respect, someone you may not quite equal but would like to equal. The boy naturally is inclined to pick the hero type that wins out over danger and risk. The girl, on the other hand, wants to win out as the misunderstood girl, one who is pure of heart and sweet, who wins the prince and all the money. This is still the basic reality of all humanity. I don't care whether it is a Yippie in the streets or a corporation president—he maintains those visions and those ideals in his mind.

Q: Do you plan far in advance how Tracy will actually catch the criminal?

Gould: I don't outline the whole story when I start. I feel if I don't know how it is going to come out, then the reader can't, and if you keep enough punch and enough interest, the intervening ground seems to be covered automatically.

Q: Do you think that Tracy in the early 30's influenced other media, such as the police procedural story in radio, movies, and novels.

Gould: Yes, but please excuse me if I seem to be a little biased. I feel that Dick Tracy has set a pattern for much of the very excellent entertainment in crime detection and police work. And I think the strip has definitely been a tremendous influence in the lives of the writers who have worked in these media.

Q: Were the mystery novels of Dashiell Hammett or any of the other authors of the hard-boiled school of writing an influence on you?

Gould: No, I got most of my inspiration from a boyhood love of Sherlock Holmes. I was also a great follower of Edgar Allen Poe. I didn't follow many of the so-called "popular" things that came in after "Dick Tracy." I followed the newspapers almost exclusively—the police news and all information about the operation of gangsters and the war against them. And it really is a war that the police are constantly engaged in.

Q: Do you see any comparison between the crimes of today and the crimes of the early 30's? Do you think there is any basic difference? In your early strips, one of the recurring crimes was kidnaping, and that seems less troublesome today.

Gould: I think there is one very good reason why that has pretty much subsided. Because of federal law you've got the Army, the Navy, and the United States Government looking for you when you kidnap somebody. This is not a little two-buck deal, like cracking a safe. Consequently, there are certain crimes that I feel have diminished automatically because of the potential punishment and pursuit that the criminal gets himself into.

Q: Criminals have come and gone—do you have any theories about why somebody goes wrong today? Some people say that poverty makes a criminal, but then again, criminals come from the wealthier classes too.

Gould: You know I don't buy too much of this. I'm not going to get into any discussion of the social situation, but I will say this: Abraham Lincoln had to do his figures on the back of a shovel with a piece of charcoal. He only got to be President.

Q: Later on in the 50's you went into science fiction—the trip to the moon, and the Moon-Maid. Why did you go in this direction?

Gould: Under no conditions did I consider this science fiction. I considered it a ramification of the potential that we are most definitely going to have to face as we explore space. We haven't scratched the surface yet. For one thing, we have got to get rid of this horse-and-buggy rocket. This thing is perhaps the biggest deterrent to real space exploration that we'll ever have. Will it go to the moon? Yes, of course. But here is a thing that involves such complications, such favorable conditions, such breathtakingly narrow margins of safety, that it must be thrown out of permanent space exploration. We have to get speed into our space transportation. The idea of taking days to go to the moon almost prohibits the practical use of the whole mission. We're going to have stations on the moon exactly like Diet Smith had them. They will be built of material that will withstand the extreme cold and heat. They will be perhaps 90 per cent underground. We will have colonies up there. I think there are things on the moon that will make it practical to be stationed there. And you can be sure, just as sure as we sit here, that we're going to have to protect what we are going to find up there. It's going to be exactly like it was when the New World was explored. Everything is going to be pirated away from the weaklings. There is going to be a very definite need to exercise power.

I was imaginative in producing people that lived there, however. I have not been completely cleared of the thought that there still may be inhabitants underground, or somewhere where they can live, such as down in a deep ravine, a place like Moon Valley. But I am sure that moon travel is here to stay and that we are going to have to get away from rockets, either through magnetic attraction or through some sort of atomic propulsion that has endless power at its command—something that is manageable. Something that won't keep the Army and the Navy and fifty thousand technicians with their fingers crossed, hoping the rocket touches ground.

Q: Well, can we get back to earth now and sort of go back a few years? In the early strips you drew grotesque criminals—was there any particular reason for doing this?

Gould: I wanted my villains to stand out definitely so that there would be no mistake who the villain was. I once received a letter from a person asking, "Why do you make your criminals so ugly?" I never looked at them as being ugly, but I'll tell you this. I think the ugliest thing in the world is the face of a man who has killed seven nurses—or who has kidnapped a child. His face to me is ugly. Or a man who has raped an old lady or young girl and robbed her of $3.40. I think this is an ugly man.

Q: We talked about the bootleggers and the Al Capones of that era. Today we don't have that kind of crime but there still is a Mafia in this country. Do you think there is an improvement in that particular area? Or have the kinds of crimes changed?

Gould: Well, I think our whole criminal problem has gotten bigger. I think the little innocent street gangs are now using the tactics employed by the Capones and their hoodlums years ago. I think that through certain court decisions the police have definitely been hamstrung, and I think there has been a psychology that has predominated in the last 20 years that has contributed to permissiveness. It's a complicated thing.

Q: Talking about the crimes of today, will Tracy ever get involved in the crimes of big business? There are a lot of swindlers within that framework, either robbing the government or robbing another company. Tracy never seems to get involved with that.

Gould: Well, most of the things that you just mentioned are today handled by the Trust Department for our government. For instance, if there is fraud in the manipulation of stocks in some big concern, the chances are very good that this would come under investigation above and beyond Dick Tracy's particular sphere. However, if in the course of this there is a homicide committed, I'm sure that old Dick would be Number One.

Q: During World War II, many comic strip heroes were placed in uniform. They joined the service in one way or another. Joe Palooka is one that comes to mind. Tracy was involved in a few cases of espionage, but did you ever think of having him join the Army?

Gould: Somebody had to stay home and take care of these crooks. And I presume that there was so much of the Army—we were so saturated with the military—that I think leaning over backwards to be patriotic and putting on a uniform was not necessary. I think Tracy's homefront activity was just as important. An example is the Brow. He was a conniving traitor and Tracy got him.

Q: In the beginning, Pat Patton was in there for a while as comic relief, but then did you give up on humor?

Gould: No, I didn't. B.O. Plenty and various situations that came up later were also humorous. But the point is, Pat Patton was made Chief when Chief Brandon resigned, and you can't have a humorous Chief of Police. He was a smart boy that worked his way up, and to the pleasure of everybody involved in the department, when Brandon resigned he was made Chief. And he suddenly became a very serious fellow.

Q: Why was he made Chief rather than Dick?

Gould: Dick turned it down. He wanted to be a plainclothes man. He liked what he was doing and Patton wanted to be Chief. It's just that simple.

Q: At one time letters were sent to you by people who couldn't understand how Tracy could afford a big mansion on a detective's salary? And then you developed a story line based on that.

Gould: Part of the success of my strip is that I have a slogan: "Bait your enemies and cater to your friends." I baited. That subject was very hot at the time; there had been some exposé in Chicago about policemen living in 20-room houses and all this. So I thought, "Gee, this is great, that will cause more damn talk. I'll have Tracy end up with a tremendous, big house." There was a period in the 40's, while the war was on, and there were many big homes being given up. I was offered a huge house built around 1920, a home that today would cost you $100,000. In 1943 it was offered to me at $5,000. Many of these old tycoons had passed on; the war came; the boys did this, and the other thing; and there stood an old house. To put it in even remotely good condition required only from $5,000 to $10,000. We explained that in the strip—Dick explained it. He said "I was offered this house." He said he paid $4,200—something like that. It had been an old mansion and he jazzed the thing up.

Q: The house itself looked so modern—like a Frank Lloyd Wright house.

Gould: I had my daughter design that; she took interior designing and she had just gotten out of college. That was a Frank Lloyd Wright house; he has two or three homes in Chicago (one of which is a classic and is being preserved) that were built, I believe, back in 1907 and 1908. They are still classics, and that's probably one reason Tracy bought it. It was a helluva buy and a fine looking place but it needed fixing up. So eventually he had a $50,000 house there, for about $10,000.

Q: What about some of the other characters. Can you predict the development of Junior's career?

Gould: He will continue to work with the police department. He is now back with his wife and child; we showed brief shots of them last Christmas. He is going to continue to be the police artist and everything is just going along like always. We're changing nothing—just continuing with a good story.

Q: Most of the stories that we picked for this book were from the period during World War II. And it seemed to me that that was the time when you really had a coterie of fantastic criminals.

Gould: We were trying very hard to fight the headlines, which were pretty sensational. In the case of Flattop, that very name was taken from the airplane carrier of the day. But I think the war was a time when that stuff came easily because so much was suggested by events and there was a very great need for furnishing relief from the damn headlines.

Q: One of the memorable parts of Tracy's life was his romance with Tess Trueheart. He finally married Tess after 18 years. Was there any motivating force for that event?

Gould: There is nothing significant at all. They were married in 1949 on Christmas Eve.

Q: Well, after they were married Tess withdrew to the background and another girl joined the force—Liz.

Gould: She is still the right-hand girl of the police department.

Q: Do you feel that this is a reflection that the wife's place is in the home?

Gould: No, you have to have policewomen. You can't handle a woman prisoner without a policewoman, and of course she's the only one we played up. Once in a while we show Liz and a uniformed policewoman working together, escorting a girl or a prisoner. She furnishes the female relief.

Q: What about Sam Catchem? Is he going to continue?

Gould: Yes, Sam will be there. In fact we have a nice deal coming up on him. You can only have one hero at a time in a story (there can't be two heroes or two heroines). Anyway I've read many letters asking why I don't let Sam Catchem do more. Why, hell, Sam Catchem is probably doing more than Tracy is, but the point is that our strip is Dick Tracy. We have to play Dick Tracy up.

Dear Reader:

October 4, 1931.

What was the state of crime in the United States during the weekend of October 3-4, 1931?

It was terrifying.

The enactment of the 18th Amendment, which had become effective more than a decade before, on January 16, 1920, and the passing of the Volstead Act for the enforcement of Prohibition, effective the next day, January 17, 1920, had triggered a National Crime Wave.

The stock market crash—a tremor on October 24, 1929 and a quake heard round the world on October 29, 1929—had triggered the Great Depression, and in its aftermath all the widespread criminal activities such a disaster breeds.

But let us look at the headlines and news stories of that October 3-4 weekend in 1931.

In New York, in a daring daylight raid, three armed men invaded the home of Deputy Police Commissioner Barron Collier and carried off a 150-pound safe containing jewels and other valuables.

A bomb exploded in a Bronx garage as dry men seized Dutch Schultz's beer.

In Brooklyn a grape truckdriver was found slain with a hatchet.

In a Monroe Street shop an undertaker's assistant was brutally murdered. The victim, his family admitted, had been making illicit liquor and was also believed to have been a collector for an East Side lottery.

In Chicago, on October 3, a football crowed jeered gang-leader Scarface Al Capone at the Northwestern-Nebraska game held in Evanston, Illinois. Capone was accompanied by his usual bodyguard of eight men and by Jack McGurn, the notorious machine gunner. (In the crowd a band of Boy Scouts ran around Capone yelling: "Yea-a-a, Al!") Capone was on trial before Federal Judge James H. Wilkerson on charges on income-tax violations—the climax to three years of investigation by the Government in an effort to rid Chicago of its Public Enemy Number One. The trial was regarded as the most important of all prosecutions of gang chieftains produced by the Prohibition era. The customary procedures would be taken against any possible attempt to assassinate Capone or some of the Government witnesses.

In New York alone, 54 homicide cases were awaiting trial, and in a vicious gun battle upstate, Vincent Coll and his gang were arrested as baby killers.

And in *The New York Times* there appeared an article titled "After All, Why Do Men Like to Drink?" by James Truslow Adams whose book, *The Epic of America,* had the lead review in that Sunday's edition, the review titled "America, Nation of Dreamers: In That Quality Mr. Adams Finds the Key to Our History."

So much for the state of Prohibition and crime on October 3-4, 1931. How about the economic and sociological state of the union? The headlines and news stories reported that—

The Pope was urging aid for the unemployed, and 75 business heads had joined in a relief drive.

In Chicago, 2000 payless schoolteachers, most of them women, cried out: "How can we buy food?"

Curb prices were still sinking, many to new lows, and the Chamber of Commerce of the United States was urging the Stock Exchange to limit short selling.

Strikebreakers and union men had rioted on Boston's docks.

Income-tax collections, Washington reported, had fallen $231 million in September.

More than 50 hospitals were facing huge 1931 deficits.

Payrolls were down 40 per cent since 1925, only six years ago.

"All over the United States banks were collapsing," wrote Walter Lippmann.

It was terrifying.

A few bright spots? Yes, there always are—if you look for them. Canon Dimnet called the Depression a "blessing in disguise." Society reported that 4000 persons attended the closing events of the Piping Rock horse show (while more than 10 million were jobless). The new Nash automobile was advertised for $795, the new Willys-Knight for $845. Marie Dressler and Lionel Barrymore were nominated for, and eventually they won, the "traditional statuettes of merit" (not yet called the Oscars). Henry Clay Frick, coke and steel pioneer, gave his mansion and art collection, valued at $50 million, to the public.

All that and more was happening.

But something else happened on October 4, 1931.

In its own way, an epic event.

In its own way, of lasting significance.

In its own way, a turning point in America.

A long-overdue counterattack.

Dick Tracy was born.

Dick Tracy was created by Chester Gould, a concerned citizen living in the Chicago area at the time. He was born in Pawnee, Oklahoma, on November 20, 1900. He had his first "professional" drawings pasted up on the window of the Pawnee *Courier Dispatch* at the age of seven—and he has been drawing ever since.

By the time he was graduated from high school in 1919, he had already taken a correspondence-school course in cartooning. His father, Gilbert Gould, publisher of a weekly newspaper, the Stillwater, Oklahoma *Advance-Democrat*, wanted Chester to become a lawyer. But Chester was committed to his life work. His father said, "Well, if you are going to be an artist, get an education; an artist without one usually dies poor." Impressed by this wisdom, Chester spent two years at Oklahoma A & M College; then with a total capital of $50 he moved to Chicago and finished his education in commerce and marketing at Northwestern University, meanwhile going to art school at night and supporting himself by drawing cartoons and doing commercial artwork.

In 1921, while still at school, he made his first submission to Captain Joseph Medill Patterson of the *Chicago Tribune-New York News* syndicate. For the next 10 years he bombarded Patterson with more than 60 comic-strip ideas—"trying everything: the beautiful girl strip, the office boy, the smart aleck, the oddball, the believe-it-or-not cartoon, even a comic feature on sports; but none of them," as Gould expresses it, "quite clicked." (You don't have to look far to find the source of Dick Tracy's determination and persistence.) Then one hot day in August 1931, while he was drawing a highly detailed Oriental rug for an advertisement, a telegram from Patterson changed Chester Gould's life. The prosaic Oriental-rug illustration was abandoned. Instead, at Patterson's request, and averaging only two hours of sleep a night for two weeks, Gould drew a month and a half of the comic strip that had finally grabbed Patterson. It was a new concept, and the first Sunday page appeared on October 4, 1931 in the *Detroit Mirror*, a tabloid owned by the *Chicago Tribune-New York News*.[1]

Thus Dick Tracy, symbol of law and order, of authority and justice, was born—"the daddy of all cops-and-robbers strips," as Stephen Becker puts it in *Comic Art in America* (1959).[2]

Gould originally called his character and strip "Plainclothes Tracy," but Patterson, with his unerring instinct for what grabbed the public, streamlined the name and title to "Dick Tracy." Dick? Probably because it was the best-known slang word for detective, and therefore the most appropriate given name. Tracy? Probably because the supersleuth was always tracing down his man.

Dick Tracy was something brand-new in comics. He broke the rules, dared to flout the taboos. "Back in 1931," says Gould, "no cartoon had ever shown a detective character fighting it out face to face with crooks via the hot lead route." Now in 1931, for the first time, comics actually showed murder, kidnaping, bloody fist fights, gory gunplay—"foul crime in detail," with all its shocking brutality.

There were misgivings, of course, on the part of newspapers and complaints from readers about the "immorality" of the strip. "It took a couple of months to catch on," Gould recalls, "then it grew like wildfire." And has been growing ever since. Readers' complaints are rare now, and official recognition has come to Dick Tracy's creator, including more than a dozen citations and awards from police departments, and the praise of J. Edgar Hoover.

Today, after 39 years of continuous comic-strip action, after a radio show, after movie serials and feature pictures (starring Ralph Byrd and Morgan Conway), and a television cartoon series, after a long line of commercial tie-ups,[3] Dick Tracy is at the peak of his popularity and success, carried in more than 600 newspapers throughout the world (*Time*, June 28, 1968, gave the figure as 800) with an estimated circulation of 50 million and a readership of at least twice that—100 million fans!

We once wrote about The Master Detective who wears a deerstalker and an Inverness cape (to the best of our recollection Sir Arthur Conan Doyle actually called them an "ear-flapped cap" and a "long gray travelling-cloak") : "Who can ever forget that tall, excessively lean man with his razorlike face and hawk's-bill of a nose . . . or the way he paced up and down that legendary room at 221B Baker Street, quickly, eagerly, his head sunk upon his chest . . . or the way he examined the scene of a crime, sometimes on all fours, his nose to the ground . . . that gaunt, dynamic figure and his incisive speech. . . ."

Compare that with a description of Dick Tracy—for in Chester Gould's mind Dick Tracy was a modernized and idealized Sherlock Holmes, the All-American boy grown up, dressed in snap-brim hat, natty striped tie, and black sack suit, whose private life is perpetually Spartan—Dick Tracy doesn't drink (he gave up smoking early in his career) and the nearest he ever comes to swearing is something like "an out-and-out alias or my name's Jeremiah!" "Who can ever forget" that tall, four-square man with his jutting (meat-chopper bulldozer) chin, his grim mouth and tight-lipped smile, his eagle's-beak of a nose . . . that absolutely honest and incorruptible defender of the faith with his Rock of Gibraltar sense of duty[4] . . . with not a soft line in his character or appearance . . . or the way he pounced, pummeled, pursued . . . or the way *he* examined the scene of a crime . . . that true-blue, indomitable, granite-featured figure and his vigorous, slangy, crisply emphatic speech . . . that iron-willed man who, ahead of his time, was never uptight, who never blew his cool.

The real-life inspiration for Dick Tracy was the state of law and order in America, especially in the big cities. In the decade preceding the birth of Dick Tracy, while the detective's character and purpose were bubbling in Chester Gould's creative cauldron, gunmen and racketeers had become, in Frederick Lewis Allen's phrase, "a national institution." A tidal wave of crime and corruption had all but submerged the big cities of this country. Chicago had been in the vanguard, but no metropolis had remained immune—New York, Detroit, San Francisco, Los Angeles, everywhere gangsterism was rampant.

The proximate cause was Prohibition. There were contributing causes (more likely to be called "symptoms" now)—confession and sex magazines, lurid movies, and the proliferation of the automobile, especially the closed car; but most historians have placed the chief blame on Prohibition.

But while the fanatical advocates of temperance had won an unbelievable victory (both when it happened and in retrospect), even unto a constitutional amendment, John Q. Public had not been reformed. Free men and women, living in an avowed democracy, decided they had the unalienable right to drink—not only water but hard liquor—and not even the Government, with a capital G, could prohibit their drinking. So, no sooner had Prohibition become the law of the land—almost, one might say, instantaneously—the people began to evade the law, then to disregard it so flagrantly, both in the letter and the spirit (no pun intended), that violating the 18th Amendment and the Volstead Act became a national pastime.

The danger in breaking one law—openly, and worse, with impunity —is the chain reaction that inexorably follows: the breaking of other laws. The populace wanted beer and booze, and beer and booze were what they got. If demand comes, can supply be far behind?

Enter, then, the bootlegger—and in almost less time than it takes to say it, the bootlegger became a romantic, even a glorified figure to a multitude of otherwise law-abiding citizens. It was not entirely an unprecedented phenomenon in American life. Americans have always had a weakness for regarding certain lawbreakers as folk heroes. (In some ways that weakness has persisted to this day.) But the demand for distilled and fermented beverages was so widespread, so urgent, that the neighborhood bootlegger, a comparatively small operator, could not supply that demand. His role quickly formed into that of a middleman.

Enter, then the Big Boys—Organized Crime. And in Chicago (now Chester Gould's home grounds) Johnny Torrio took over as early as 1920. But even he proved not big enough—or tough enough or ruthless enough or cynical enough. The man supposed to be Torrio's lieutenant, one Alphonse Capone, became the czar of bootlegging, and before he was finally sent to Alcatraz for income tax evasion—not long after Dick Tracy's debut as a crimebuster—he was the acknowledged kingpin of gambling, vice, and the rackets. Break one law and all laws become vulnerable.

Let us take a kaleidoscope-montage look at the 10 years of crime during which Chester Gould sought and found his colorful pen-and-ink hero. Your memory will fill in the historical collage, and the names and words will evoke images of the criminal Life and Times of the United States, 1920-1931.

The Hall-Mills murder case. The Sacco-Vanzetti *cause célèbre*. The bull market on Wall Street, encouraging recklessness, false values, self-indulgence.

The Problem of the Younger Generation (sound familiar?).

Speakeasies—10,000 in Chicago alone.

"The world is crumbling" (sound familiar?).

Scandal, political corruption in high places, Teapot Dome.

Skyrocketing stock market: Radio Corporation of America—a 1928 low of 85¼, a 1929 high of 549. (By November 13, 1929 RCA had dropped to 28, by 1932 to a low of 2½.)

Great God Business. Great God Money—and nothing smaller than millions.

Leopold and Loeb trial. Florida real estate boom—and bust. *Homo boobiens* (H. L. Mencken's phrase).

Prohibition: rum-ships, smuggling ("just off the boat")—hijacking, Thompson sub-machine guns ("typewriters"), illegal stills ("alky-cooking"), hip flasks, "Joe sent me," "noble experiment" (President Hoover's phrase), taken "for a ride," "rubbing out," thugs, torpedoes, heisters, hoodlums.

In 1927 alone, according to Fred D. Pasley, Al Capone's biographer, the Capone gang's income amounted to $105 million ($60 million from beer and liquor, $25 million from gambling, $10 million from vice, dance-halls, roadhouses, $10 million from rackets). By 1929 there were 91 different rackets in Chicago, with an estimated total cost to the citizenry of $150 million a year.

Bribery, "fixed" juries, politicians (including judges) in the crooks' pockets ("everybody greased from the big shots down"), graft, conspiracy, extortion, "protection," arson, bombing.

St. Valentine's Day massacre (February 14, 1929).

The stock market hit its 1929 bottom on November 13. "In a few short weeks the crash had blown into thin air 30 *billion* dollars[5]—a sum almost as great as the entire cost to the United States of its participation in the (First) World War, and nearly twice as great as the entire national debt."

Panic. Depression. By 1930 one out of every four factory employees was out of work. Bootleggers were openly doing business in the Senate Office Building in Washington, D.C. Enforcement of Prohibition was "a mockery."

Depression widening, deepening. Jobless men, exhausted savings, relief (if any funds were available), bankruptcies, smokeless factory chimneys, beggars and panhandlers, breadlines and soup kitchens, "Hoovervilles" (communities of squatters living in makeshift shacks on vacant city lots), cardboard insoles to cover holes in shoes, able-bodied men selling apples on street corners, hunger, disillusionment, despair.

And the despair finding its outlet in violence and crime.

A poll of the "paramount problems of the United States" taken the same year Dick Tracy was born rated the major problems as: No. 1: Prohibition. No. 2: Administration of Justice. No. 3: Lawlessness.[6]

All these ingredients stewed and brewed until the melting pot of life in America boiled over.

District Attorney Crain of New York: "Racketeers have their hands on everything from the cradle to the grave—from babies' milk to funeral coaches."

And in those ten years Chester Gould had been saying to himself: "Why can't they get those birds? Why, say, if I were a cop, I'd shoot them right down on the spot." Still quoting Mr. Gould: "The public demand was for less red tape, more direct action in dealing with criminals."

So Chester Gould, concerned citizen and artist,[7] did something about it. And inevitably what he did reflected the hard, tough times that had America in its gangster grip. Chester Gould produced a contemporary knight in shining armor who was ready, willing, and able to fight the criminal with, if necessary, the criminal's own weapons, to fight the toughs with equal or even greater toughness. Chester Gould created Dick Tracy to meet the desperate need of the times. Dick Tracy's job was to regain the almost vanished respect for the law and to be the instrument of his enforcement. As Gould once said in an interview: "I decided that if the police couldn't catch the gangsters, I'd create a fellow who would."

The second major influence on the creation of Dick Tracy was a new literary form emerging during the 1920's in the United States. It is said that "Art imitates Nature," and this new literary form mirrored real life. Its style and substance sprang directly from the national crimino-economic condition, transforming (more precisely, translating) the brutality and violence, the poverty and despair, into fiction. And like its real-life source it was a uniquely American product. We know it now as the hardboiled detective-action story.[8]

In March 1920 H. L. Mencken and George Jean Nathan founded a pulp magazine they called "The Black Mask"; but they quickly got bored with it—they had seemingly bigger fish to fry—and sold out for a profit. Under its first editor, F. M. Osborne, "The Black Mask" was a typical pulp. But when George W. Sutton, Jr., ably assisted by Harry North, took over the editorship in October 1922, Prohibition was nearly three years old and the human condition was no longer an ominous outline. The grotesque features in the face of crime were now clearly visible.

Sutton and North, who were early exponents of "telling it like it is," began to develop a kind of fiction that exposed the criminal life and times of "the land of the free and the home of the brave." It is significant that Sutton bought and published the first crime-detective stories written by Dashiell Hammett, Carroll John Daly, and Erle Stanley Gardner whose characters were, in Philip Durham's phrase, "rugged individualists righting social wrongs." The new style, according to William F. Nolan, was "bitter, tough, unsentimental, uncompromisingly realistic, reflecting the violence of its time . . . a bare-knuckles approach."

In April 1924, Phil Cody became the editor of "The Black Mask," and with him, Erle Stanley Gardner has said, "the action type of detective story took a long strike forward." There was plenty of real-life action to draw on: Capone treating the police of Chicago as if they were Keystone Cops; Dion O'Banion's funeral, gangster-style—a $10,000 casket and 26 truckloads of flowers, including one modest wreath with a card signed "From Al"; the capers of Bugs Moran, Hymie Weiss, Three-Gun Alterie. A Chicago reporter wrote: "We are living by the code of the Dark Ages."

In November 1926, Joseph "Cap" T. Shaw undertook the cultivation of "Black Mask" (the "The" was dropped, a small indication of Shaw's insistence on economy of expression), and under his editorship "Black Mask" reached its fullest flower in capturing "the illusion of reality," in portraying characters who talked tough and, more important to the truth of the times, acted tough. Shad had "meditated on the possibility of creating a new type of detective story," and he had searched among the contributors to "The Black Mask" for a special spark of originality. He chose as leader of "a new school in writing" an ex-Pinkerton agent, Dashiell Hammett, who like Ernest Hemingway had been "trying to make fictional events truer than life." Hammett became "the ace performer" (Raymond Chandler's later appraisal), and, quoting William F. Nolan again, "Hammett brilliantly defined the troubled aspects of the period of open criminal warfare, poverty, and festering political corruption."

So the stage was set for Chester Gould's creation of Dick Tracy: in real life, the national crime wave caused first by Prohibition and then by the Great Depression; in literature, "Black Mask" and such "drawn from life" books as Hammett's *Red Harvest, The Dain Curse, The Maltese Falcon,* and such mainstream novels as W. R. Burnett's *Little Caesar* and William Faulkner's *Sanctuary.* Whether or not Chester Gould ever read "Black Mask" in the decade before Dick Tracy's birth in print, or read books by the hardboiled writers of the 20's, he knew what was going on

—not only in real life but in the "intensely concerned, emotionally aroused" (editor Shaw), "fast, terse narratives" (Ron Goulart) that were reflecting "this action-filled rawness, this world of lusty hoodlumism" (Jules Feiffer). Gould *felt* it—it had been growing in him for 10 years. It was in the climate. No citizen who gave a damn in those days could be oblivious of it. The time had come—it was almost too late—to restore law and order, to reestablish authority and justice. The time had come for Race Williams, The Continental Op, Sam Spade—and Dick Tracy.

Now, just what kind of detective is Dick Tracy? Where does he fit in the mystery genre? We know he is the father of the detective comic strip —but what is his place in the larger field of fictional detection? Was he influential not only as a crimino-cultural force but as a crimino-literary force?

Well, we began to dig into the Dick Tracy canon, to refresh our faded memories. And we learned something we had never even suspected. Dick Tracy *is* important in mystery-story history—he was a "first," a genuine "first." We came up with a startling discovery.

Most of us consider Dick Tracy strictly an action-detective as handy with his fists as with his gun; a rugged, hardboiled detective who can, as Chester Gould intended, take everything the criminals dish out and dish it right back—sometimes in spades. But the truth is, Dick Tracy is more than just a ball of fire in furious action. When you renew your acquaintance with him in the comics reproduced in this volume, you will find that Dick Tracy is a thinking detective too, that surprisingly he combines the "intellectual" school with the "physical," and that he is a proficient craftsman of true-life police techniques.

Exactly how does Dick Tracy detect? He is, of course, a determined and persistent legman. He investigates and interrogates. But technically he goes far beyond the usual limits of action-detection. Let's look at the printed record.

Dick Tracy introduced the two-way wrist radio, in the strip of January 21, 1946. When it first appeared, the two-way wrist radio was science-fictional; today it is science-factual.

Dick Tracy was the first to make use of television as a means of crime detection. He was the first to use closed-circuit television (which he called "teleguard") to monitor possible criminal activities, and the first to adapt television as a burglar alarm.

In his 39 years of crime-fighting, Dick Tracy's methods have been mental as well as muscular, deductive as well as dynamic. His techniques have included the newest procedures known to science in the identification of fingerprints ("bringing them out with the iodine blowgun" or "lifting them by the wet-film process"). He is expert enough in his job to look for fingerprints in seemingly unlikely places—on a victim's fingernails, for example, where the killer's prints might have been left if there had been a struggle, or on a car's rearview mirror where prints might have been left if the criminal had absent-mindedly adjusted the mirror. And Tracy is no less professional in identification through footprints.

You will learn that Dick Tracy is completely at home in a police laboratory, completely expert in the use of chemistry, telescope camera, lie detector, microscope, magnifying glass (or jeweler's loupe), and other scientific tools. His "hunches" turn out to be based on keen observation of minutiae. He is thoroughly skilled in such non-action detection as ballistics and handwriting analysis, is capable of shrewd psychological experiments, and he knows police-department regulations and F.B.I. textbooks by heart. He answers an official summons by helicopter, and is always one of the first, if not the first, to take advantage of every innovation in police procedure—for instance, in 1937, the "use of the tracer bullet in making a capture in a darkened room."

The whole picture of Dick Tracy's daily battle with crime is "a realistic picture of modern police work" (to quote Robert M. Yoder). Chester Gould has been called "a perfectionist who takes pride in the accuracy and researching" of even the most minute details, and as a result there are no unsolved crimes in Dick Tracy's casebook.

Now what does all this add up to? We tend to remember Dick Tracy's fisticuffs, gunshots ("rat-tat-tat"), frantic chases, and "old movie-serial" cliffhangers, and tend to forget his resourceful on-the-scene and laboratory techniques. And the part we tend to forget is an important aspect of Dick Tracy the detective—the aspect that stamps him a procedural detective as much as an action-detective. As George Perry and Alan Aldridge wrote in *The Penguin Book of Comics,* "The criminals and crimes in Dick Tracy may be wildly exaggerated; his police work is sound and orthodox."

Where, then, does Dick Tracy rank in the line of fiction's procedural detectives? In prose (that is, in books and magazines) we have established the chronological order of procedural detectives. In their own times many fictional sleuths operated in essence as procedural detectives. For examples: Emile Gaboriau's Lecoq (1866) whose methods were, by today's standards, rather primitive; the various detectives who never slept and whose exploits, chiefly imagined, were chronicled by Allan Pinkerton (1874); R. Austin Freeman's Dr. Thorndyke (1907) whose scientific modus operandi is still valid; Freeman Wills Crofts's Inspector French (1924) whose cases emphasized legwork and painstaking investigation; and a cogent argument can be advanced that William MacHarg's O'Malley started the modern procedural *trend*—his "affairs" began to appear in

Collier's magazine in 1932. But it is generally agreed that Lawrence Treat made the most significant contribution to the development of the contemporary police-procedural in prose. It was his novel, *V As in Victim* (1945)—10 years ahead of J. J. Marric's (John Creasey's) first Commander Gideon novel, *Gideon's Day,* and 11 years ahead of Ed McBain's first 87th Precinct novel, *Cop Hater*—in which the police-procedural came of age. In reviewing Treat's first procedural story the late Anthony Boucher wrote: "In its unpretentious way, this may be an epoch-making book, marking a fresh, new, realistic approach to police procedure." And later Mr. Boucher wrote: "The prime pioneer in the naturalistic novel of police procedure was Lawrence Treat whose stories were not only far ahead of their times but admirable in themselves."

Where, then, does Dick Tracy fit in this order? Dick Tracy first appeared in print on October 4, 1931—*one year ahead* of MacHarg, the trend-maker; *14 years ahead* of Treat, the "prime pioneer"; *24 years ahead* of Marric (Creasey) ; *25 years ahead* of McBain. Now bear in mind that Dick Tracy was not conceived to be a vigilante or a private eye. Actually, Captain Patterson instructed Chester Gould to "start him off as an ordinary young fellow who has dedicated himself to the pursuit of thugs who have murdered the father of the girl he loves; after he succeeds in bringing them to justice, turn him into a professional police officer." So in the beginning, for only the first few weeks of his career, Dick Tracy was a "hard-hitting amateur who dealt with criminals with fists, blackjack, or gun; his prowess won him an appointment as a city detective," a member of the plainclothes squad.

Nor was Dick Tracy, in the historical sequence of fictional sleuths, the first action-detective or the first hardboiled detective. But he was, as we have shown—and this is the startling discovery—the world's first procedural detective of fiction, in the modern sense. And the discovery is even more startling when we realize that the world's first procedural detective made his debut not in prose but in pictures, that he entered the mainstream of the mystery genre not in a book or magazine but in a newspaper.

A newspaper comic strip is not that far removed from book or magazine fiction. All the elements of fiction are present in the comic strip: story line, characterization, exposition, dialogue (usually in "balloons"), conflict, development of plot, denouement—all enhanced, in the comic strip, by concrete visualization. Chester Gould has said that he "considers himself a teller of tales"—and that is true, both in pictures and words, although he naturally thinks in terms of panels rather than paragraphs. Pictorially, Gould has a comic-book genius for drawing grotesquely caricatured faces and heads and for inventing grotesquely Dickensian character-names[9] to match the faces and heads. And Gould's plots have all the excitement and suspense of "thriller" fiction. So Dick Tracy is blood-brother in the royal line of fictional detectives, and an authentic "first" in the history of the form. Indeed, despite his 39 years of unceasing pursuit and punishment of criminals, Dick Tracy has not really aged—he remains forever young and "with it." In recent adventures he has even been blasting off into outer space, encapsulated in a spaceship, to trace down astro-crooks, thus anticipating what could be the next major development in the mystery field—the blending of science fiction and detective fiction, a "wedding of genres" (to use the phrase of Allen J. Hubin, mystery critic of *The New York Times*). But then, as we have proved, Dick Tracy has been "anticipating" ever since his birth in print 39 years ago—Chester Gould, always proud of his ahead-of-the-times viewpoint, once said, "I try to anticipate things."

Now join Dick Tracy in some of his danger-packed, breathtaking, hair's-breadth adventures and escapes—Dick Tracy versus Organized Crime—Dick Tracy slugged, pistol-whipped, tortured, burned, beaten, frozen, chloroformed, gassed, near-drowned, knocked out, pressurized, de-pressurized, dynamited, dragged by a car at 60 miles an hour, stabbed, shot (by actual count, 27 bullet wounds in the first 24 years), mangled and crushed (especially his shooting hand), victim of concussions, fractures (usually compound), cracked ribs, dislocated hip—in the course of 39 years of crimebusting, a veritable encyclopedia of harrowing experiences, "grisly business," "gruesome, sinister, fiendish havoc" (a combination of Chester Gould's own words), and impossible-to-get-out-of predicaments ("hot spots")—Tracy was once sealed in paraffin and has often been buried alive ("It's curtains—I'm sunk!"). Dick Tracy, the scourge of law-breakers, the terror of the underworld, the nemesis of crime and evil, whose philosophy is: "Little crimes lead to big crimes" and "crime does not pay." Dick Tracy, the indestructible man.

Sic durat gloria mundi.

Ellery Queen

ENDNOTES

[1] One week later, on October 12, 1931, Dick Tracy made his debut in the New York *Daily News*. His first appearance in the *Chicago Tribune* was delayed until March 22, 1932.

[2] Dick Tracy's comic-strip forerunners[2a] included Eddie Eks's Alex the Cop, Hugh Doyle's Mr. Wiseguy the Detective, and Gus Mager's Hawkshaw the Detective, the last a burlesque of Sherlock Holmes complete with magnifying glass, pipe, Sherlockian garb, and farcical deductions. *Après* Dick Tracy *le déluge:* here are some of the many comic-strip detectives who followed in Tracy's footsteps: Lyman Anderson's Inspector Wade; Eddie Sullivan's and Charlie Schmidt's Pinkerton, Jr. (retitled Radio Patrol, later called Sergeant Pat of Radio Patrol); Alexander Gillespie Raymond's and Dashiell Hammett's Secret Agent X-9 (the agent's name was Phil Corrigan); Frank E. Leonard's Mickey Finn (about the family life of a detective); Alfred Andriola's Charlie Chan, and later, Kerry Drake; Ray Bailey's Bruce Gentry (an airline detective); Alex Raymond's Rip Kirby (a gentleman action-detective); and let us not forget Al Capp's Fearless Fosdick, a parody of Dick Tracy (once Fearless Fosdick, in an unsuccessful attempt to arrest a balloon vendor for not having a license, killed 42 people!). To say nothing of the Western-type detectives like Fran Striker's and Charles Flanders' The Lone Ranger and James Guilford Swinnerton's Rocky Mason, Government Marshal; and another offshoot, Allen Dean's King of the Royal Mounted; and such "superdetectives" designed to "instill fear into the hearts of the underworld" like Jerry Siegel's and Joe Shuster's Superman, Bob Kane's Batman and Robin, and Bert Whitman's The Green Hornet.

[2a] The world's first fictional detective, Edgar Allan Poe's C. Auguste Dupin (1841), had his forerunners too: among them, Daniel (in the Bible), Voltaire's Zadig (1747), William Leggett's Jim Buckhorn (1827), François Eugène Vidocq (1828), and Charles Dickens' "officers from Bow Street," Blathers and Duff (1838).

[3] The commercial tie-ups include radios, watches, burglar-alarm and detective kits, masks, wallets, guns of various kinds, secret money pockets, flashlights, clothing of various kinds, cameras, binoculars, fountain pens, candy, puzzles, a Gravel Gertie banjo, a Sparkle Plenty doll ($3 million in sales the first year), Sparkle Plenty Christmas-tree lights—more than 60 different by-products. Imagine, Dick Tracy candy!

[4] If we correctly understand Stanley Burnshaw in his *The Seamless Web* (1970) and some of the authorities he quotes, the creation of a redeeming character is one of man's attempts to heal the alienation of man from the world, from his fellow-man, and from himself.

[5] Inflationary (and Cautionary) Note, 41 years later: without a cataclysmic crash "the value of shares on major exchanges was down about 300 billion dollars" in the past 18 months (*U.S. News & World Report*, June 8, 1970).

[6] Lest you forget the present: the F.B.I.'s 1969 statistics for the United States indicate one murder committed every 36 minutes, 9 serious crimes every minute, one auto theft every 36 seconds (seconds, not minutes), one larceny every 21 seconds, one burglary every 16 seconds. The 1969 crime rate was 11 per cent over 1968, and so far in 1970 the crime epidemic has been hitting new highs ("Serious reported crime increased 13 per cent the first quarter of 1970"—*The New York Times*, June 23, 1970).

[7] Is "artist" too strong a word? Pretentious? From Jack O'Brian's syndicated column of May 15, 1970: "The Museum of Modern Art bought several of Bob Kane's original 'Batman' drawings." Chester Gould's draftsmanship improved quickly: more interesting composition, more "shading," more "angle" shots; and as Gould's drawing became stronger, more confident, more authoritative, Dick Tracy as a character became stronger, more confident, more authoritative.

[8] Paraphrasing Stendhal: "A hardboiled detective-action story is a mirror riding the streets of a city"; or to use a quotation from Matthew Arnold, it is "a criticism of life."

[9] Chester Gould's Rogues Gallery is "a veritable bestiary of monsters and grotesques . . . used as a sign of their moral ugliness and criminality . . . and to facilitate an easy recognition of good and evil" (quoting Professor Arthur A. Berger). Here is a partial listing of Chester Gould's *dramatis personae*, including "ingenious fiends" and "criminal freaks": Spaldoni (the first archvillain), Pruneface, Flattop (Sr. and Jr.), Rhodent, Piggy, Supeena, Mumbles, Itchy, Hypo, Laffy, Nifty, Shoulders, Spots, Crutch, Measles, Gargles, Flyface, Littleface, Shaky, Deafy, "Nothing'" Yonson, F. (Ankle) Redrum, B. O. Plenty (and his father Morin), Gravel Gertie, Sparkle Plenty (B. O.'s and Gravel's daughter), Nilon Hoze, Haf-and-Haf (shades of L. Frank Baum's *Sky Island!*), The Brow, The Midget, The Blank, The Mole, B-B Eyes, Doc Hump, Breathless Mahoney, 88 Keyes, Joe Period, Ribs Mocco, Vitamin Flintheart, Diet Smith, "Stooge" Viller, Ugly Christine, Big Frost, Mrs. Volts, T. V. Wiggles, Dr. Plain, Crewy Lou, Intro. . . . As other have pointed out, naming a character after his or her vice, trait, or appearance is an old literary device, found in the oldest morality plays. But, then, what are detective stories but modern morality plays?

E.Q.

THE FIRST APPEARANCE OF DICK TRACY

DICK TRACY's first appearance was on Sunday, October 4, 1931 in the *Detroit Mirror*. This appearance was followed by another page on October 11 in the same newspaper. On Monday, October 12, 1931, the daily strip began in the *New York News*.

THE FIRST EPISODE

October 12, 1931–November 13, 1931

THE FIRST EPISODE

6

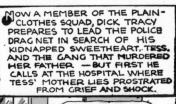

THE FIRST EPISODE

THE FIRST EPISODE

WELL, EVERY'TING IS SET, JOE - WE'LL DO THAT PAYROLL JOB ANY DAY NOW - JIST GOTTA WAIT FER DE HIGH SIGN FROM BIG BOY.

OH, I SEE - BIG BOY SETS OFF THE WORKS, DOES HE?

YEAH.

AND DE GET-AWAY IS GONNA BE A CINCH! BIG BOY IS HAVIN' A DAME DRIVE TH' CAR. - YOU KNOW, COPS IS APT TO BE LESS SUSPICIOUS OF A DAME. CHEEZE! DIS IS GONNA BE A PUSH-OVER

WHO IS THE DAME RIBS?

HOW DO I KNOW? MUST BE SOME BABE HE GOT HIS HANDS ON SOME PLACE AND HE WANTS 'ER TO WORK OUT HER BOARD BILL - HE WOULDN'T SEND HIS REAL DAME ON A DANGEROUS JOB LIKE DAT

YES, THIS IS MR. PECK OF THE WESTERN COMPANY.

THIS IS DICK TRACY OF THE PLAIN CLOTHES BUREAU - I MUST SEE YOU IMMEDIATELY! MEET ME IN HALF AN HOUR AT THE HILO CLUB.

LATER

MR. TRACY? WHAT DOES THIS MEAN SIR? YOU'VE GIVEN ME QUITE A FRIGHT.

YOUR CASHIER IS TO BE ROBBED OF HIS PAYROLL WITHIN THE NEXT TWENTY-FOUR HOURS - IF PLANS OF THE MOST DESPERATE GANG IN TOWN ARE CARRIED OUT.

BUT I ASSURE YOU NO SUCH THING WILL HAPPEN AND WE CAN JAIL THE WHOLE OUTFIT IF YOU WILL COOPERATE. - NOW MY PLAN - - -

WHILE BACK IN THEIR GANGLAND ROOM, WHERE TRACY IS KNOWN ONLY AS "JOE," RIBS MOCCO AND SPIKE CONTEMPLATE THE FUTURE WITH MUCH ENTHUSIASM.

CHEE, I CAN JUST SEE THE LOOK ON THAT PUNK, JOES, FACE WHEN HE DON'T COME IN FOR NO SPLIT! HO.HO. - AND ME TELLIN' HIM HE'D GIT FIVE GRAND! SAY, HE OUGHTA PAY US FER LETTIN' HIM WORK ON THIS HIGH CLASS JOB.

ALL RIGHT, SISTER, YER LIFE AIN'T WORTH TWO CENTS UNLESS YOU OBEY ORDERS AND GET BACK HERE SAFELY WITH TH' DOUGH. I'VE GOT MEN STATIONED ALL ALONG THE STREET WHERE YOU DRIVE AND IF YOU PULL ANY FUNNY STUFF IT'S JUST TOO BAD.

- AND I'M LEAVIN' YOU HERE, KID. DRIVE STRAIGHT DOWN TO THIRTY-NINTH STREET - WAIT UNDER TH' BIG CLOCK TWENTY MINUTES, THEN DRIVE SLOWLY OVER PAST THE WESTERN COMPANY BUILDING.

STRAIGHT AHEAD, BABY - AND NO FUNNY BUSINESS!

DON'T FERGIT YER INSTRUCTIONS!

ALL SET, JOE? GOT YER ROD, YOU GUYS?

YEAH.

YEAH.

YOU GO ON IN - ASK TH' CASHIER TO CHANGE DAT TWENTY FER YU - ME AN' SPIKE 'LL FOLLER YU. DO YER STUFF OR Y'WON'T WALK OUT ALIVE.

OKAY.

IT'S HERE - MR. PECK. KEEP YOUR NERVE NOW FOR A MINUTE.

CASHIER

'STICK 'EM UP' EVERYBODY - STICK 'EM - WHAT -

DROP THOSE GUNS, YOU HOODLUMS

CASHIER

THE FIRST EPISODE

THE BLANK

1937–1938

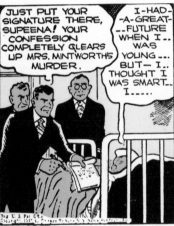

THE BLANK

THE BLANK

THE BLANK

WELL, WE'VE BEEN AWAY FROM YOUR DETECTIVE HERO'S GARAGE 20 MINUTES. IN ANOTHER QUARTER HOUR I SHALL LET YOU OUT.

OH! THERE'S TRACY GOING HOME FROM SHOW-UP IN THE SQUAD CAR. HEY—

BUMP

I BELIEVE I ASKED YOU TO KEEP YOUR MOUTH SHUT! I'M NOT IN THE HABIT OF SAVING YOUNGSTERS' LIVES AND THEN HAVING THEM CALL THE COPS.

I'M GOING TO LET YOU OUT. I BELIEVE BY NOW THE CARBON MONOXIDE HAS COMPLETED ITS WORK BACK IN YOUR FRIEND'S GARAGE.

AND YOU MAY TAKE DOWN THIS CAR'S LICENSE NUMBER IF YOU WISH. YOU'LL FIND IT BELONGS TO A DENTIST LIVING UP TOWN. I "COMMANDEERED" IT FOR THE EVENING.

10-29

THIS IS THE OPPOSITE SIDE OF THE CITY FROM WHERE MR. TRACY LIVES— SO YOU'D BETTER HOP A STREET CAR. HERE'S A DIME.

THE MAN WITHOUT A FACE! OF ALL THE—!! OH BOY! I'VE GOT TO GET BACK TO TRACY'S PLACE!

WELL, GOODNIGHT TRACY— SEE YOU TOMORROW.

HEY, TRACY— WAIT— WAIT!

WHERE HAVE YOU BEEN? WHAT'S THE MATTER?

QUICK! BACK TO YOUR GARAGE— I'LL EXPLAIN LATER—

10-30

GREAT SCOTT! MY GARAGE— MY CAR RUNNING— WHAT!

LOOK! SUPEENA'S MEN! LOOK!

A MAN WITHOUT A FACE, I SAW HIM— HIS NAME'S THE "BLANK"— HE—

SHUT OFF THE MOTOR, PAT! GOOD HEAVENS THEY'RE—

I'LL OPEN THE DOOR TO CLEAR THE AIR.

AFTER THE GRUESOME DISCOVERY IN TRACY'S GARAGE THE DETECTIVE TAKES JUNIOR INTO HIS APARTMENT TO GET THE COMPLETE STORY FROM HIM

AT THE HEAD OF THE APARTMENT STEPS THEY ARE CONFRONTED BY THE FACELESS ONE HIMSELF, WHO TELLS TRACY HE TOO IS DEVOTING HIS LIFE TO CATCHING CROOKS!

WHEN I STARTED AFTER HIM HE PULLED A SMOKE-THROWING DEVICE FROM HIS POCKET AND FILLED THE PLACE WITH SMOKE.

LOOK—THERE HE GOES.

HE SAID THOSE TWO GASSED IN YOUR GARAGE WERE JUST A BEGINNING! WHO IS HE?

21

THE BLANK

THE BLANK

24

THE BLANK

WHILE I'M WAITING FOR PAT TO RETURN WITH MY FINGER-PRINT LIFTING EQUIPMENT, I'LL MAKE A HURRIED EXAMINATION OF DALTON.

HM! THREE SHOTS! AND ALL FIRED FROM A POSITION NEAR THE GROUND.

HOW CAN YOU TELL THAT, TRACY?

IN THIS WAY. THE MARKS OF THE BULLETS' EXIT FROM THE BODY ARE ALL ABOVE THE POINTS OF ENTRANCE.

THAT WOULD INDICATE DALTON RECOGNIZED THE "BLANK", THEY HAD A HAND TO HAND SCUFFLE, THE "BLANK" WAS THROWN TO THE GROUND AND HE FIRED FROM THAT POSITION.

HERE YOU ARE, TRACY.

PAT, YOU ACCOMPANY DALTON'S BODY TO THE MORGUE. I'LL STAY HERE AND GET THAT HAND-PRINT OF THE "BLANK."

CLANCY, YOU CAN STICK HERE - AND GIVE ME A HAND.

GLAD TO, MR. TRACY. I'M ANXIOUS TO SEE WHAT THIS WET-FILM PROCESS IS.

FIRST, WE DUST ANY EXCESS DIRT OFF THE PRINT. YOU KNOW, CLANCY, BY THIS PROCESS IT'S POSSIBLE TO LIFT THE PRINT OF A SHOE OFF OF LINOLEUM.

GOSH, THAT'S WONDERFUL.

TURN THE GARAGE LIGHTS OFF WHILE I TAKE A PIECE OF UNEXPOSED FILM FROM THIS PACK AND MOISTEN IT.

YES, CLANCY, IN LIFTING A HANDPRINT BY THIS PROCESS, YOU FIRST MOISTEN AN UNEXPOSED CAMERA FILM, AWAY FROM LIGHT.

THEN YOU BLOT THE FILM BETWEEN TWO BLOTTER PAPERS TO REMOVE THE EXCESS MOISTURE.

OF COURSE, I USE A FLASHLIGHT WITH A RED GLASS IN IT TO SEE WHERE TO PLACE THE FILM

BY PRESSING THE MOIST FILM GENTLY, EVERY MINUTE PART OF THE FINGERPRINT ADHERES TO THE EMULSION. AS I TOLD YOU BEFORE, THE PROCESS IS SO DELICATE A SHOE PRINT CAN BE PICKED OFF OF LINOLEUM. NOW, WE MUST DEVELOP THE FILM.

STEP IN HERE, PAT, WILL YOU?

YES SIREE!

WELL, THERE IT IS PAT, THE HANDPRINT OF THE "BLANK"! I JUST FINISHED DEVELOPING AND ENLARGING PART OF IT.

NOW I'M GOING TO PUT THIS ON A LANTERN SLIDE SO I CAN BLOW IT UP ON A SCREEN FOR STUDY.

MEANWHILE, I WANT YOU TO SEARCH THE FINGERPRINT FILES AND GET ME EVERYTHING IN HIS CLASSIFICATION. HERE IT IS —
18 16 R O REF 12
32 W M2 30

THE BLANK

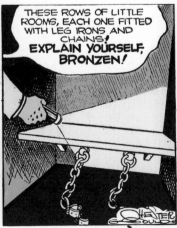

THE BLANK

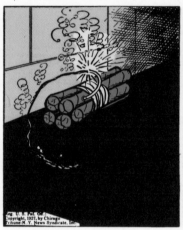

THE BLANK

GREAT SCOTT! HE'S GOING TO CRUSH US TO DEATH WITH COMPRESSED AIR. I CAN SCARCELY BREATHE!

12-23

HA! THE PRESSURE IS MOUNTING BEAUTIFULLY! I'LL TAKE ONE LOOK AT THE GENERATOR IN THE ROOM BELOW.

PERFECT! PERFECT! 110 VOLTS -- AND EVERYTHING RUNNING SMOOTHLY.

THAT EXPLOSION DID ME A GREAT FAVOR WHEN IT HURLED ME BACK UNDER THE PIER. OTHERWISE I'D BE A PRISONER WITH TRACY AND BRONZEN.

12-24

AS IT WAS, I CAME TO JUST IN TIME TO SEE THE "BLANK" MARCH DICK AND "STUD" BELOW DECK.

I'VE GOT TO GET INSIDE AND THERE'S JUST ONE WAY! I MUST SMASH THE GLASS WITH MY SHOE — AND TAKE A CHANCE THAT THE ROAR OF THAT GENERATOR WILL COVER UP THE NOISE.

ON BEHALF OF OUR FRIENDS WHO AT THE MOMENT ARE OCCUPIED WITH OTHER MATTERS — I WANT TO WISH YOU ALL A MERRY MERRY CHRISTMAS

HA! IT'S A TIGHT SQUEEZE, BUT I GUESS I CAN MAKE IT.

12-25

AHA! THEY CAN'T SURVIVE ANOTHER FIVE MINUTES AND THE BEAUTY OF IT IS — COMPRESSED AIR LEAVES NO FINGERPRINTS! THEIR BODIES WON'T CONTAIN A SINGLE CLUE!

WHY, THE INSANE -- ...FIEND--! I'VE GOT TO ACT FAST!

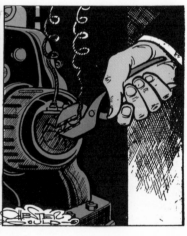

CRAWLING INTO THE BOAT THROUGH A PORTHOLE, PAT PATTON SEIZES A PAIR OF WIRE SNIPPERS AND CUTS THE CONDUIT LEADING FROM THE ELECTRIC GENERATOR. THEN, GRABBING A DIVER'S HELMET, HE HIDES NEAR THE STAIRWAY AS THE "BLANK" COMES STOMPING DOWN STAIRS.

WHAT'S WRONG -HEY! WHO'S DOWN HERE?

12-27

THERE, MR. BLANK! IF THAT 60 POUND DIVER'S HELMET DOESN'T STOP YOU — IT SHOULD AT LEAST SLOW YOU UP ENOUGH FOR US TO SEE WHAT YOU LOOK LIKE.

THE BLANK

THERE, MR. "BLANK".. YOU'RE HANDCUFFED... AND YOU'RE STILL OUT LIKE A LIGHT.

1-1-38

CAESAR'S GHOST! WHAT A FACE! OW!.. IT'S FLESH.... AND IT ISN'T! GOSH.... I CAN'T STAND TO TOUCH IT.....UGH.

I'D BETTER GET UPSTAIRS AND SEE HOW TRACY'S DOING. I'LL LET HIM UNRAVEL THE "BLANK'S" FACE!

WE'RE OKAY, NOW, PAT.. OPEN THE DOOR.

PICKING UP THE STILL UNCONSCIOUS "BLANK", TRACY AND PAT HEAR A NOISE ABOVE DECK, AND HURRY UPSTAIRS JUST IN TIME TO SEE "STUD" BRONZEN DISAPPEAR BENEATH A DISTANT PIER. HE HAD JUMPED OVERBOARD.

1-3-38

WELL, I'M CERTAINLY SORRY BRONZEN GOT AWAY FROM US - BUT OUR PRESENT JOB IS TO GET THIS FELLOW REDRUM TO HEADQUARTERS AND INVESTIGATE HIS MYSTERIOUS FACE.

TRACY, YOU TAKE THE "BLANK". TO HEADQUARTERS. I'LL RUN DOWN ALONG THE RIVER FRONT AND SEE IF I CAN HEAD OFF BRONZEN WHEN HE COMES UP.

GOOD! GO TO IT.

YES SIR! IT LOOKS TO ME JUST AS THOUGH HE'S GOT FLESH-COLORED CHEESE CLOTH PASTED ON HIS FACE. BY JOVE - THAT'S WHAT IT IS!

UGH! IT IS CLOTH..... PASTED RIGHT ON HIS FACE!

YES - PAT.!

I WASN'T ABLE TO SPOT BRONZEN. SHOULD I COME IN?

NO.

I'VE JUST SENT TWO COMMERCIAL DIVERS DOWN THERE. HAVE THEM USE THAT DIVING EQUIPMENT IN BRONZEN'S BOAT AND BRING UP ANY EVIDENCE THEY CAN GET THEIR HANDS ON FROM THE BOAT THAT WAS BLOWN UP.

HE'S COMING TO.

CARTHY, GET THE BOTTLE OF ETHER TO REMOVE THAT ADHESIVE SUBSTANCE - AND A PAN OF WATER. WE'RE GOING TO TAKE OFF THAT CLOTH.

YES SIR!

SIT STILL, REDRUM. DON'T MOVE!

1-5-38

WE'RE GOING TO REMOVE YOUR FALSE FRONT, LITTLE MAN. - RIGHT NOW.

THIS IS JUST A LITTLE ETHER. I'LL DISSOLVE THAT ADHESIVE STUFF - AND IF YOU DON'T HOLD STILL - I'LL PUT THE BOTTLE A LITTLE CLOSER TO YOUR NOSE.

OKAY - NOW HOLD 'IM, BOYS!

MARY X

1940

MARY X

BRAVO! MORE! MORE! SWING IT, SIS.

WHAT A VOICE YOU HAVE! YOU WOWED 'EM!

10 MINUTES LATER IN THE DRESSING ROOM.

SHE'S A SENSATION! I'LL PUT HER IN MY BAND.

GOOD! YOU CAN CALL HER--SAY--ER--.. "MARY X".

MARY X! THAT'S IT! WHY, YOU'LL BE--WELL, FOR--LOOK! SHE'S ASLEEP!

YES--THE KID'S BEEN THROUGH SOME KIND OF AN ORDEAL, ALL RIGHT. BUT WHERE AND WHEN?

SAY, RUDY! SLIP OFF HER SHOES AND LET ME HAVE THEM. THERE'S SOMETHING CLINGING TO THE SOLES.

HERB, MARY X, IS AN ENTIRE NEW OUTFIT FOR YOU TO WEAR.

BUT MY SHOES? WHERE ARE THEY?

OH, I HAVE A BRAND NEW PAIR FOR YOU. LOOK!

OH, THEY'RE BEAUTIFUL!

MEANWHILE, MARY X'S OTHER SHOES ARE IN TRACY'S HANDS AT HEADQUARTERS.

DO YOU THINK HER SHOES WILL TELL YOU WHO SHE IS?

HM?? MAYBE

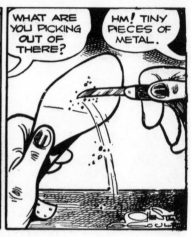
WHAT ARE YOU PICKING OUT OF THERE?

HM! TINY PIECES OF METAL.

AS THE AMNESIA GIRL, "MARY X", SWINGS OUT ON A REFRAIN TO THE DELIGHT OF THE CAFE AUDIENCE, A SHOT PIERCES THE AIR, STRIKING THE "MIKE" IN FRONT OF THE GIRL.

BANG!

OH.. OH.....

THAT WAS A DELIBERATE SHOT! SOME ONE TRIED TO KILL "MARY X".

HEY! GRAB HIM BACK THERE...GRAB HIM!

WHO?

WHERE IS HE?

HOME, JERRY.

YES, SIR.

WHOEVER FIRED THAT SHOT STOOD BACK HERE.

LET'S LOOK OUT FRONT.

DID ANYONE LEAVE HERE WITHIN THE LAST MINUTE, BOB?

WHY, ER--YOWSA, MR. TRACY. I SEE MR. MASON GO.

MR. MASON--WHO'S HE?

HE'S A BIG SHOT GENT'MAN THAT COMES HERE. EVERYBODY KNOWS MR. MASON YOWSA.

PICK ME UP AT THE OFFICE IN 2 HOURS, AND GET THIS--BRING ALL THE LATE EDITIONS OF THE NEWSPAPERS WITH YOU, UNDERSTAND?

YES, SIR.

MARY X

DO YOU KNOW HIM?

YES, YES —IT'S FREEZ...MY BUSINESS PARTNER.

DO YOU HAVE ANY IDEA HOW HE COULD HAVE MET HIS DEATH?

NOT AT ALL! WHY, HE'S SUPPOSED TO BE ON A BUSINESS TRIP IN THE EAST! I...I THOUGHT THAT'S WHERE HE WAS

DO YOU KNOW THIS GIRL, MR. MASON?

ER..NO..NO, I DON'T BELIEVE I'VE SEEN HER B-B-BEFORE.

HAVE YOU EVER SEEN HIM, MARY?

I...I DON'T KNOW. I..I CAN'T REMEMBER ...I CAN'T... REME-M....

THAT'S WHAT I SAID, WE'RE ALL GOING INTO THE MACHINE SHOP OF YOUR FACTORY, AND TRY TO BRING BACK THIS GIRL'S MEMORY.

YOU'RE TALKING NONSENSE, TRACY.

I'M GOING TO TRY AN EXPERIMENT. I WANT YOU TO STAND HERE, MASON. AND, MARY, I WANT YOU TO STAND OVER THERE.

PAT, WHEN I TOUCH MY HAND TO MY HAT, I WANT YOU TO FIRE THIS PISTOL. IT'S LOADED WITH A BLANK.

OKAY.

WHILE TRACY TALKS TO PAT —— A HAND GOES UP TO A CHAIN—A CHAIN THAT REACHES BACK TO A HEAVY STEEL HOIST DIRECTLY OVER MARY X'S HEAD!!

WHAT'S THAT NOISE?

LOOK! THAT HOIST!

CLATTER CLATTER

OUT OF THE WAY, MARY!

IT GRAZED HER HEAD. SHE'S OUT! HAND ME A GLASS OF WATER, PAT.

ARE YOU OKAY, MARY?

MARY? ...MY NAME'S NOT MARY. ..I...I'M LEOLA SUNNY. I...I USED TO WORK HERE.

THE CATCH MUST HAVE SLIPPED.

YEAH?

SH, SH..QUIET! HE TRIED TO KILL YOU WITH THAT HOIST. BUT THE BLOW ONLY RESTORED YOUR MEMORY. EASY NOW!

I...I REMEMBER EVERYTHING...THIS IS WHERE HE KILLED...

SH.. SH!

THAT WAS A RATHER FUNNY ACCIDENT, MASON. IT HAD JUST THE OPPOSITE RESULT FROM WHAT YOU PLANNED.

WHAT DO YOU MEAN?

AT THIS INSTANT, A DARK FIGURE BEGINS TO ASCEND AN IRON STAIRWAY AT THE REAR OF THE FACTORY. THAT STAIRWAY LEADS TO A SKYLIGHT OVERLOOKING THE MACHINE SHOP FLOOR.

Doolb later confessed that he shot Mason because he did not deliver the crooked gambling equipment as promised to the gambling syndicate.

JEROME TROHS AND MAMMA

1940

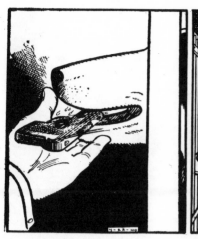

JEROME TROHS AND MAMMA

JEROME TROHS AND MAMMA

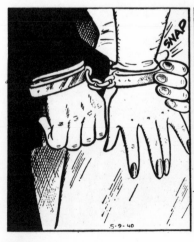

JEROME TROHS AND MAMMA

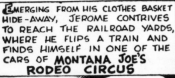

EMERGING FROM HIS CLOTHES BASKET HIDE-AWAY, JEROME CONTRIVES TO REACH THE RAILROAD YARDS, WHERE HE FLIPS A TRAIN AND FINDS HIMSELF IN ONE OF THE CARS OF **MONTANA JOE'S** **RODEO CIRCUS**

WHAT? A MIDGET COW HAND!

CERTAINLY! HAVEN'T YOU BOYS EVER HEARD OF **JOE ATOM**? THAT'S ME. I'M A BRONCO BUSTER.

WAIT TILL I GET THE BOSS!

HEY, MONTANA, COME BACK TO THE OTHER CAR — GOT SOMETHING TO SHOW YOU!

WHAT? A MIDGET COW HAND? WH-- WHY, YOU'LL BE A **SENSATION** — — A KNOCKOUT-- A BOMBSHELL IN THE RODEO BUSINESS! YOU'RE HIRED!

JOE ATOM— THAT'S MY PROFESSIONAL NAME. WHY, I CAN BULLDOG A STEER TWO HUNDRED TIMES **MY OWN WEIGHT!**

YOU'RE GREAT, ATOM. YOU'RE **COLOSSAL**, YOU'LL SLAY 'EM!

THIS IS THE SLICKEST GETAWAY I EVER MADE. THE COPS WILL **NEVER** LOOK FOR ME ON A TRAIN WITH A RODEO.

'SOON AS WE REACH THE WEST, I CAN DITCH THIS MOB AND HIDE OUT FOR THE SUMMER.

WE'LL BILL YOU IN 24-SHEETS ALL OVER THE WEST. WE'LL HAVE YOU POSE WITH THE GOVERNOR. WE'LL HAVE YOU

GET THE WARDROBE MAN IN HERE. HAVE 'IM CUT DOWN A PAIR OF CHAPS TO FIT ATOM. HAVE 'IM REBLOCK ONE OF THOSE 10-GALLON SOMBREROS. **JOE ATOM RIDES AGAIN!**

THAT'S IT, JAKE! FIT 'IM UP WITH A WHOLE OUTFIT. MEASURE 'IM GOOD. GIVE HIM THE BEST.

I'LL HOLD THE COAT, IF YOU DON'T MIND.

AND BACK HOME!

WHY, THE LITTLE RAT! HE **DITCHED** ME. HE THREW ME OVER. I-I COULD **BREAK HIS NECK!** I-I COULD-

LISTEN, MAMMA. QUIT PUTTING ON AN **ACT!** WE'LL FIND YOUR POCKET EDITION ALL RIGHT. BUT WHEN WE DO— **WE'LL** DO THE BREAKING, **NOT** YOU.

A **MIDGET COW HAND!** WHY, YOU'LL BLAST THE RODEO BUSINESS! AH-HA - HA -- I **LOVE** YOU, ATOM!

WELL, THERE YOU ARE, MONTANA! HOW DOES HE LOOK? CHAPS, VEST, HAT, BOOTS AND GUN.

AHA-AHA!

LISTEN, YOU MUGS, THIS THING'S GONE FAR ENOUGH! WHAT DO YOU THINK I AM? I JUST ROBBED AN ARMORED CAR. I'M NO BOY SCOUT. STOP THIS TRAIN, I'M SCRAMMING!

COLOSSAL! **STUPENDOUS!** **WHAT** A LITTLE **ACTOR!** A BOON TO THE ENTIRE **RODEO TRADE!**

BOY'S, WE'RE SET FOR THE SUMMER. THIS WILL BE OUR **STAR ACT!**

AW NUTS!

YIPPIE! YOWEE!

61

JEROME TROHS AND MAMMA

LET US SHIFT THE SCENE OF OUR STORY FOR A FEW MOMENTS TO A TOURIST CAMP HIGH UP ON A MOUNTAIN NOT FAR FROM DOGGIE CITY...

HI-MOUNTAIN TOURIST CABINS

YES, JASPER, WE MADE A TERRIBLE MISTAKE WHEN WE BOUGHT THIS TOURIST CAMP. NO ONE EVER COMES UP HERE.

IT'S TOO ISOLATED. WE'RE TOO FAR FROM THE HIGHWAY!

NOW BE PATIENT, MA. THE SUMMER'S BARELY BEGUN.

WHY, EVEN JUST ONE LITTLE OLD CUSTOMER WOULD HELP! SO WE COULD FEEL THERE WAS SOMETHING COMING IN!

HM!

?

UM-M HOWDY, PARDNER!

OH, HELLO THERE! ER---YES, SIR. HEL-LO!

DO YOU HAVE CABINS FOR RENT HERE?

YES, SIR! NICE CLEAN CABINS-THE VERY BEST SIR!

OUR FIRST CUSTOMER, JASPER!

WHAT DID I TELL YOU, MA!

GET CLEAN SHEETS, MA --AND TWO CLEAN PILLOW CASES! BRING A PAIL OF FRESH WATER AND BATH TOWELS - AND SCRUB OUT NUMBER ONE. STEP THIS WAY, SIR!

HM! NOT CROWDED, THAT'S GOOD.

GOODNIGHT, SIR. HOPE YOU SLEEP WELL. HOPE IT'S QUIET ENOUGH FOR YOU, SIR.

HOPE YOU HAVE PLENTY OF COVERS. IF YOU WANT ANYTHING JUST CALL. WELL, GOOD NIGHT!

WHAT A DUMP! BUT I'VE STILL GOT DOUGH. I CAN HIDE OUT HERE FOR A FEW MONTHS TILL THE HEAT'S OFF.

AND NOW- BACK IN THE CITY, AT THE WOMAN'S PRISON.

IF I COULD ONLY GET MY HAND ON THAT JEROME -WOW! OR IF I ONLY KNEW WHERE HE WAS - I'D TELL THE ---

THE WEEKLY FREE MOVIES WILL BE SHOWN IN THE DINING HALL IN TEN MINUTES. ALL WHO CARE TO ATTEND STAND AT ATTENTION AT YOUR CELL DOORS.

MOVIES, BAH! OH, WELL, I'LL SEE THEM.

SCENE: WOMEN'S PRISON DINING HALL WHERE THE INMATES ARE VIEWING THE WEEKLY MOVIE SHOW...

IT'S HIM! YES-- IT'S HIM!

WHAT AILS YOU? HAVE YOU GONE NUTS?

THAT NEWSREEL! THAT NEWSREEL! STOP IT! FIND OUT WHERE IT WAS TAKEN. THERE'S A MAN IN THERE THAT—

WHAT ARE YOU TALKING ABOUT? ARE YOU OUT OF YOUR HEAD?

PERHAPS THIS IS A MENTAL CASE.

HOLD THAT NEWS-REEL AND CALL DETECTIVE TRACY! I WANT HIM TO SEE IT!

YES, SIR! THAT'S WHAT I'LL DO! I'LL OFFER TO BUY THE PLACE. IT'LL MAKE A PERMANENT HIDEOUT FOR ME. I'LL BUY 'EM OUT!

62

BUT I TELL YOU, THAT MIDGET IS JEROME - MY JEROME. THE SAME LITTLE GUY THAT DOUBLE-CROSSED ME AND LEFT ME.

THE FACE ISN'T DISTINCT ENOUGH FOR IDENTIFICATION, BUT I'LL TELL YOU WHAT I'LL DO - I'LL TELEPHONE THE RODEO OWNER AND FIND OUT WHO THE LITTLE GUY IS.

YES, MISTER, THE TOURIST CAMP'S ALL YOURS. THAT GOVERNMENT DEED IS ALL THE PAPER YOU'LL EVER NEED.

THANKS FOR THE THREE THOUSAND DOLLARS.

GOOD-BYE!

THREE THOUSAND DOLLARS! HA! HA! WHY, PICKING THAT OLD GUY'S HIP POCKET WAS AS EASY AS SLAPPING A SLEEPING BABY. AH! HA! HAW! HA!

THINK OF IT, MA, WE SOLD THAT OLD LEMON OF A TOURIST CAMP FOR THREE THOUSAND DOLLARS!

I CAN HARDLY BELIEVE IT. LET ME SEE THE MONEY. I JUST WANT TO TOUCH IT.

WHAT? - MY - MY - WALLET! MY POCKETBOOK! IT'S GONE!

IT WAS RIGHT HERE IN MY HIP POCKET WHEN WE LEFT! WE'VE BEEN ROBBED!

OH, IT MUST BE RIGHT HERE IN THE SEAT, PA.

AND AT THE WOMEN'S PRISON...

OH--OH! --I CAN'T STAND IT. THE PAIN-- THE PAIN!

WHAT IN THE WORLD AILS HER? HEY, GIRLIE!

LET'S GO INSIDE.

OH, THE PAIN! ---MY SIDE-- MY RIGHT SIDE!

HELP ME GET HER UP ON THE BUNK.

HM! MAYBE THE APPENDIX. THAT GOES HARD WITH A FAT PERSON.

WE'D BETTER CALL THE PRISON DOCTOR!

WHILE THEY'RE GONE, I'LL STEAM MY FACE IN THIS HOT WATER.

TWENTY MINUTES LATER....

YES - SHE'S FEVERISH! LOOKS LIKE AN ACUTE CASE. WE'D BETTER GET HER OUT OF HERE!

OH, MY SIDE! --MY SIDE!

MY MONEY! MY THREE THOUSAND DOLLARS! IT MUST BE HERE SOMEWHERE. I MISSED IT AS SOON AS I GOT INTO MY CAR.

I DON'T KNOW A THING ABOUT IT, MISTER.

LISTEN, IT COULDN'T HAVE WALKED OFF! IT WAS IN MY HIP POCKET WHEN I SHOOK HANDS WITH YOU -YOU -

GET BACK IN THAT CAR HILL-BILLY! AND GET OFF MY PROPERTY!

STRAIGHT TO THE SHERIFF IN DOGGIE CITY! THAT'S WHERE WE'RE GOING. WE'VE BEEN ROBBED!

AND IN DOGGIE CITY...

WHAT'S THAT? A NEW POLICE CIRCULAR, SHERIFF?

YEAH-JUST CAME IN THE MORNING MAIL. IT'S ABOUT SOME MIDGET THEY'RE LOOKIN' FER BACK EAST!

JEROME TROHS AND MAMMA

JEROME TROHS AND MAMMA

JEROME TROHS AND MAMMA

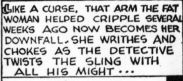

68

LITTLE FACE FINNY

1941

WITH TRIGGER SAFELY TUCKED AWAY, TRACY STARTS TO HIS DOCTOR'S OFFICE FOR A FINAL CHECKUP OF HIS INJURED HIP IN HOPE THAT HE MAY DISCARD HIS CRUTCH WHEN—

PUT TRIGGER BACK IN HIS CELL, MURPHY, WHILE I ANSWER THE PHONE.

YEAH? NO KIDDING! I'LL BE RIGHT OVER, TRACY.

10 MIN. LATER

JUST AS THE BOYS CROSSED CENTRAL AVENUE, A RUNAWAY TROLLEY BUS CRASHED INTO A GARAGE—WITH THE DRIVER SHOT. LOOK! THERE IT IS.

THERE'S TRACY, TOO!

IT WAS AN EMPTY BUS GOING BACK TO THE CAR BARNS. THE DRIVER HAS A BULLET IN HIS CHEST.

TAKE HIM TO THE EMERGENCY HOSPITAL, BOYS. AND LISTEN CAREFULLY TO WHAT HE SAYS WHEN HE STARTS TO COME TO.

WHEN PAT AND I FIRST SAW THE BUS, IT WAS WEAVING BACK AND FORTH ABOUT A BLOCK DOWN THE STREET.

WHEN WE REACHED THE BUS, THE DRIVER WAS LYING RIGHT THERE ON THE FLOOR JUST AS YOU SAW HIM.

DID YOU SEE ANYONE STEP OFF THE BUS JUST BEFORE IT STARTED TO WEAVE?

NOT A SOUL, CHIEF AND WHY WASN'T THAT GUY NEAR THE WHEEL?

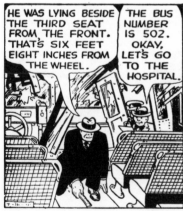

HE WAS LYING BESIDE THE THIRD SEAT FROM THE FRONT. THAT'S SIX FEET EIGHT INCHES FROM THE WHEEL.

THE BUS NUMBER IS 502. OKAY, LET'S GO TO THE HOSPITAL.

AND AT THE HOSPITAL.

THERE'S A BULLET NEAR THE LEFT LUNG. WE'LL OPERATE IN TWENTY MINUTES.

THE BUS DRIVER IS RESTING EASY, DOCTOR. I'LL STAND BY.

AH, THERE HE IS.

TELL ME WHAT YOU DID WITH THEM? COME ON-QUICK! WHERE DID YOU PUT THEM? WHERE DID—

UH—— UH—— —I—— ONE OF THE SEATS.

IN ONE OF THE SEATS—— ONE OF THE SEATS——

THANKS, PAL!

WE'RE READY TO TAKE HIM TO THE OPERATING ROOM.

DOCTOR! DID YOU SEE A FIGURE DROP DOWN FROM THAT WINDOW SILL?

NONSENSE! IT WAS JUST YOUR IMAGINATION, NURSE.

HERE'S MR. TRACY.

BUT WE'RE JUST PREPARING TO TAKE HIM TO THE OPERATING ROOM.

NEVERTHELESS, I WANT TO HAVE A FEW WORDS WITH HIM BEFORE HE GOES TO THE OPERATING ROOM. DRIVER, CAN YOU HEAR ME?

'UH—— UH——

LITTLE FACE FINNY

I WAS IN CAHOOTS WITH--A STICK-UP GANG. THE ROBBERIES WERE TIMED--SO THAT I COULD PICK UP THE GUNMEN AS--I MADE MY OWL RUN BACK TO THE YARDS AT--- MIDNIGHT.

I-I THINK I'D BETTER CALL THE POLICE.

IT WOULD BE BETTER IF YOU TOLD THEM.

NO-- NO-- THERE ISN'T TIME--WRITE! --- I-I'M DYING ---

MR. STANLEY'S ROOM IS RIGHT DOWN THERE.

OKAY, LET'S GO!

THE NAMES OF THE OTHERS ARE -

OH, HELLO!

WE'RE RELATIVES. I'M HIS AUNT. WE WANT TO SEE HIM ALONE.

BUT, HE'S-

I SAID, WE WANT TO SEE HIM ALONE! NOW-

WHO IS IT? WHO IS IT?

HELLO, MICKY!

HELP! HELP! POLICE! POLICE!

OKAY- OUT THE WINDOW! THAT'S THAT.

THE CAR'S THIS WAY.

THAT ENDS THE CONFESSION.

THEY WERE DRESSED IN WOMEN'S CLOTHES --TWO OF THEM. OH, IT'S TERRIBLE.

IT SOUNDED LIKE AT LEAST A DOZEN SHOTS.

CALL THE-

YOU'RE TOO LATE, MR. TRACY.

WE HEARD THE SHOTS DOWN IN THE LOBBY. WHERE'S HIS ROOM?

AND IN ANOTHER PART OF TOWN.

LITTLE FACE, WE'VE DONE OUR JOB!

GOOD! SIT DOWN, I WANT TO TALK TO YOU.

LITTLE FACE FINNY

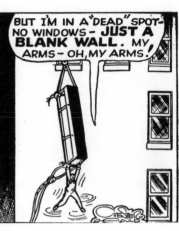

LITTLE FACE FINNY

INTO THE PARK LAGOON DIVES THE TAXI.

THE FRONT END OF THE CAR SETTLES AND DISAPPEARS BENEATH THE WATER.

THEN SLOWLY THE REAR OF THE VEHICLE BEGINS TO GO DOWN AS THE WHEELS PRESS INTO THE MUD.

LOWER AND LOWER! LITTLE FACE'S HEAD IS ONLY TWO INCHES FROM THE WATER — THEN ONE INCH — THEN SLOWLY —

IT'S OKAY, MISTER. MAYBE WE CAN PRY YOU LOOSE WITH THIS TWO-BY-FOUR.

DON'T SHAKE THE CAB TOO MUCH OR IT'LL TAKE ME UNDER.

BRING THE PULMOTOR. I SAW A DRIVER IN THE FRONT SEAT AS IT WENT IN.

MEANWHILE, TRACY AND PAT ARE PASSING THROUGH THE PARK, TAKING LOMA TO THE CIRCUS TENT AT THE OTHER SIDE OF TOWN.

HEY! LOOK OVER THERE!

WAIT A MINUTE, PAT. I'D BETTER TAKE A LOOK.

THE CAB DRIVER AND LITTLE FACE ARE RESCUED FROM THE SUBMERGED CAB JUST AS TRACY, PAT AND LOMA STOP TO VIEW THE EXCITEMENT. THEN SUDDENLY —

HE-HE-GRABBED MY GUN!

SURE, I'M LITTLE FACE! YOU NEVER SAW ME BEFORE, COPPER, SO YOU BETTER TAKE A GOOD LOOK NOW! I'M GOING TO MAKE A GETAWAY USING YOUR AERIAL PERFORMER PAL FOR A SHIELD.

WHAT ARE YOU DOING? JUST RUBBERNECKING? OKAY, OPEN THAT REAR DOOR.

NOW DRIVE! AND I MEAN DRIVE! STEP ON IT! NORTHWEST ACROSS THE RIVER AND OUT INTO THE COUNTRY.

WELL, ARE WE GOING TO LET HIM GET AWAY WITH IT?

LET'S GO!

WHY THE DIRTY ~!

TURN THE CAR AROUND, PAT. LOMA SAVED MY LIFE — NOW IT'S MY TURN.

LITTLE FACE FINNY

'S FUNNY! A WHILE AGO I FELT LIKE I WAS FREEZING -- BUT NOW I DON'T FEEL SO COLD.

AND IT'S TEN BELOW! HAH! I'LL JUST WRAP UP IN THESE STIFF HIDES AND SNOOZE TILL MORNING.

KINDA COZY IN THESE NICE -- WARM COW HIDES -- NICE WARM.--

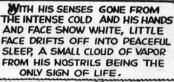

WITH HIS SENSES GONE FROM THE INTENSE COLD AND HIS HANDS AND FACE SNOW WHITE, LITTLE FACE DRIFTS OFF INTO PEACEFUL SLEEP, A SMALL CLOUD OF VAPOR FROM HIS NOSTRILS BEING THE ONLY SIGN OF LIFE.

YOU'VE FOUND NO TRACE OF LITTLE FACE, EH?

NOT A THING, CHIEF. HIS TRAIL ENDED IN THE MIDDLE OF THE STREET WHERE THOSE BLOOD SPOTS STOPPED.

DON'T WORRY, HE'S PROBABLY LYING SOMEWHERE COOLING OFF FOR A WHILE, TRACY. HE'LL TURN UP.

"COOLING OFF" IS RIGHT, CHIEF! IN FACT, TEN BELOW ZERO OR FIFTY BELOW ZERO - NEITHER WOULD MAKE MUCH DIFFERENCE RIGHT NOW TO LITTLE FACE.

AS A NEW DAY DAWNS AND TRUCK DRIVERS PREPARE TO OPEN THE COLD STORAGE LOCKER FOR THE DAY'S WORK -

CHARLEY! DO YOU SEE WHAT I SEE?

GET MORE ICE - WE'VE GOT TO SOAK THE FROZEN PARTS IN ICE WATER. I TELL YOU THAT'S THE ONLY WAY WE CAN SAVE HIM

BUT, CHARLEY, WHO IS HE AND WHY DID YOU BRING HIM HERE?

I TELL YOU HE'S A BIG SHOT GANGSTER! AND I'M GOING TO MAKE HIM PAY ME BIG DOUGH FOR SAVING HIS LIFE.

I FOUND HIM IN THE LOCKER STORAGE PLANT - HALF FROZEN. INSTEAD OF CALLING THE COPS, I BROUGHT HIM HERE.

BUT WHAT ABOUT YOUR TRUCK DRIVING JOB? DID YOU GIVE THAT UP?

LISTEN, IF I CAN SAVE HIS LIFE IT OUGHT TO BE WORTH AT LEAST TEN GRAND. IT WOULD TAKE THREE YEARS OF DRIVING A TRUCK TO MAKE THAT MUCH.

CHARLEY SHOULDN'T HAVE TAKEN THAT GUY TO HIS HOME. THAT SCHEME OF HIS IS BLACKMAIL. HE'LL GET-

MORNING, THOMPSON!

-ER-- MORNING- BOSS!

SAY, WHAT'S GOING ON? WHAT'S HAPPENED TO THAT BUNDLE OF HIDES? AND WHAT ARE YOU DOING SCRUBBING THE FLOOR?

-ER-OH-

THAT LOOKS LIKE BLOOD. SINCE WHEN WAS THERE ANY WARM MEAT IN HERE?

--ER-- WELL, OKAY, BOSS, I MIGHT AS WELL TELL YOU.

LITTLE FACE FINNY

BUT, CHARLEY, YOU'RE HARBORING A GANGSTER! YOU'RE LEAVING YOUR LAWABIDING JOB AS A TRUCK DRIVER TO TURN CROOK.

SHUT UP!

LOOK! HE'S TURNING BLACK! THIS ICE ISN'T DOING ANY GOOD.

I'D BETTER CALL THE DOCTOR. I DON'T WANT A DEAD MAN ON MY HANDS.

MY EARS! MY HANDS! OH, THE PAIN — I CAN'T STAND IT!

EASY, LITTLEFACE, THE DOCTOR'S ON HIS WAY.

THIS IS KLASTER OF THE COLD STORAGE LOCKER COMPANY. SEND YOUR BEST DETECTIVE DOWN HERE, WILL YOU?

CLOSE DOOR.

ONE OF MY DRIVERS SAID A GUY BY THE NAME OF LITTLEFACE FINNEY SPENT THE NIGHT IN HERE. IT'S QUITE A MYSTERY.

LITTLEFACE?

LITTLE-FACE?

COME IN, DOC.

WHERE IN THE WORLD WOULD A MAN GET FROST-BITE THIS TIME OF YEAR?

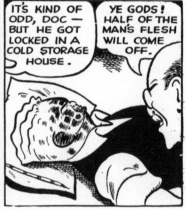

IT'S KIND OF ODD, DOC — BUT HE GOT LOCKED IN A COLD STORAGE HOUSE.

YE GODS! HALF OF THE MAN'S FLESH WILL COME OFF.

THIS IS THE WORST CASE I EVER SAW!

IS IT? WILL HE LIVE, DOC?

I CAN'T PROMISE ANYTHING. HOWEVER, I THINK I CAN SAVE HIS HANDS.

THE MOST IMPORTANT THING IN FREEZING IS TO RESTORE THE CIRCULATION TO THE REMAINING LIVE TISSUE.

YEAH?

IN THE CASE OF HIS EARS THAT'S IMPOSSIBLE. THE EARS WILL HAVE TO BE AMPUTATED.

YES, IT CERTAINLY IS A MYSTERY, MR. TRACY. COME THIS WAY.

FIRST OF ALL, YOU SAY THIS MAN'S NAME WAS LITTLEFACE FINNEY. HOW DO YOU KNOW THAT?

HERE'S A CARD MY PARTNER TOOK OUT OF THE MAN'S POCKET.

HOW DID LITTLEFACE GET IN HERE? AND WHO IS THIS "PARTNER" YOU'RE TALKING ABOUT?

MY PARTNER'S NAME IS CHARLEY YENOM. HE SAID HE WAS GOING TO TAKE LITTLEFACE TO HIS HOME.

LOOK OUT FOR THAT BLOOD, TRACY.

THIS FELLOW'S ANKLE WAS CUT. THAT'S WHERE HE BLED.

THAT WAS LITTLEFACE, ALL RIGHT!

82

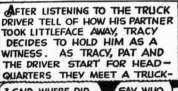

AFTER LISTENING TO THE TRUCK DRIVER TELL OF HOW HIS PARTNER TOOK LITTLEFACE AWAY, TRACY DECIDES TO HOLD HIM AS A WITNESS. AS TRACY, PAT AND THE DRIVER START FOR HEAD-QUARTERS THEY MEET A TRUCK—

I SAID, WHERE DID YOU PICK UP THOSE COW HIDES?

SAY, WHO ARE YOU?

.IM FROM HEADQUARTERS, MISTER, AND I WANT YOU TO SHOW ME JUST WHERE YOU GOT THOSE!

HEADQUARTERS? OH, THAT'S DIFFERENT. SURE, I'LL SHOW YOU!

PAT, WE'VE STRUCK IT! TAKE THIS MAN TO THE STATION AND WAIT THERE TILL I CALL. I'M GOING WITH THE GARBAGE DRIVER.

YOU SAY—THEY AMPUTATED MY EARS?

YEAH, BUT YOU'RE ALIVE, LITTLEFACE YOU'RE ALIVE! AND FOR TEN GRAND I WON'T CALL THE COPS!

YEAH, THAT'S WHERE I PICKED UP THE OLD COW HIDES. RIGHT BEHIND THAT BUILDING.

I SEE. THANKS, OLD MAN!

I'LL LOOK AT THE MAIL BOXES IN THE LOBBY FIRST TO SEE WHAT FLOOR HE'S LOCATED ON.

"HERE WE ARE. "CHARLEY YENOM- THIRD FLOOR.

I'LL GIVE YOU THREE MINUTES TO MAKE UP YOUR MIND. EITHER YOU CALL YOUR PALS AND HAVE THEM SEND OVER TEN THOUSAND DOLLARS OR I CALL THE COPS!

THIS IS LITTLEFACE. YEAH--LISTEN, MUSSEL, I'VE GOT TO HAVE TEN GRAND. UNDERSTAND? IT'S A CASE OF LIFE AND DEATH!

I SEE, LITTLEFACE. YEAH-- I SEE--A TRUCK AND A RUG, EH? OKAY- WE GOT YOU.

HELLO, TRACY. WE GOT YOUR CALL.

I LOCATED THE FLAT. THAT'S IT RIGHT ACROSS THE STREET. NOW, HERE'S OUR PLAN—

WE'D BETTER TAKE THE BIG RUG. IT'S CLEANER — AND, LITTLEFACE DON'T LIKE DIRT.

I'LL PHONE THE BOYS TO MEET YOU WITH THE DOUGH.

NOW, IS EVERYTHING CLEAR? PAT AND I WILL TAKE THE FRONT. YOU, THE ALLEY, SMITTY. AND, OLSON, WATCH THE SIDE!

HEY, LOOK!

JUST A RUG CLEANER'S TRUCK. WE'LL WAIT TILL HE PULLS AWAY.

YEAH! HE'S TAKING A RUG IN.

WHERE ARE YOU GOING, TRACY?

WHILE THE DRIVER'S UPSTAIRS, I'LL LOOK THAT TRUCK OVER. YOU MEN WAIT HERE!

WELL, HERE I AM, LITTLEFACE!

COME ON! PAY THIS MUG AND GET ME OUT OF HERE.

LITTLE FACE FINNY

84

THE MOLE

1941

THE MOLE

"STEVE, THE TRAMP" THEY CALL ME-AND TO ALL THE BOYS AND GIRLS IN AMERICA I WANT TO REPEAT, YOU CAN'T WIN AT CRIME.

I'M GOING STRAIGHT NOW! AND TO THOSE TWO CERTAIN PEOPLE- WHO I HOPE ARE LISTENING IN - I WANT TO SAY, PLEASE BELIEVE ME.

THOSE TWO CERTAIN PEOPLE TRACY-ARE US! STEVE'S TALKIN' TO US!

WHAT LUCK THAT WE HAPPENED TO BE TUNED IN ON THIS PROGRAM!

OPERATOR, GET ME THE "PERSONALS" STUDIO OF THE CHAIN BROADCASTING COMPANY QUICK, PLEASE.

YES, THIS IS GABE KOLDER OF THE "PERSONALS" PROGRAM. WHAT? OH, YES, HOW ARE YOU? WHAT? YOU'D LIKE TO SPEAK TO STEVE?

FOR ME?

WE'RE VERY HAPPY AND VERY PROUD OF YOU, STEVE. I WANTED TO BE THE FIRST TO CONGRATULATE YOU!

MR. TRACY!

WE WANT TO SEE YOU, STEVE: WHEN ARE YOU COMING TO SEE US?

AS SOON AS I'VE PROVED WHAT I SAID OVER THE AIR. I WANT TO GET A JOB AND MAKE SOME MONEY. I WANT TO GET SOME NEW CLOTHES.

REMEMBER, STEVE, YOU HAVE FIFTY DOLLARS COMING FOR YOUR BROADCAST!

WHETHER YOU HAVE A JOB OR NOT, STEVE, I'D LIKE TO SEE YOU. I MIGHT BE ABLE TO GIVE YOU A LITTLE FINANCIAL AID UNTIL YOU GET ON YOUR FEET.

NO-NO, MR. TRACY! I COULDN'T DO THAT. I COULDN'T- I COULDN'T-

CLICK

HE-HE HUNG UP ON ME!

HERE YOU ARE, STEVE. FIFTY DOLLARS FOR APPEARING ON OUR PROGRAM. GOOD-BYE AND LOTS OF LUCK.

FIFTY DOLLARS! THANK YOU! THANK YOU!

FIFTY DOLLARS! OH, BOY, THAT'S A LOT OF MONEY. I KNOW WHAT I'LL DO. I'LL GO TO OCEAN PARK.

I'LL GET SOME HOT DOGS - AND RIDE THE ROLLER COASTER. I'LL TAKE UP WHERE I LEFT OFF WHEN I WAS A KID!

ONE HOUR LATER.

HOT DOGS AND COTTON CANDY! LET'S GO!

THE MOLE

TAKE 'EM AWAY!

OH, BOY! MY FIRST ROLLER COASTER RIDE SINCE I WAS A KID!

AS THE CAR STEVE IS RIDING IN STARTS OUT, ANOTHER CAR FINISHES THE RIDE AND PULLS UP TO THE LOADING PLATFORM.

JUNIOR, I'LL NEVER DO THAT AGAIN AS LONG AS I LIVE! MY! OH, MY!

GEE, MISS TESS, THAT'S THE SWELLEST RIDE IN THE WHOLE PARK. OH, BOY!

WE'VE PATRONIZED ABOUT EVERYTHING, JUNIOR. SUPPOSE WE START HOME. IT'S BEEN A BIG DAY.

WHAT DO YOU SAY? LET'S TRY THE BINGO GAME BEFORE WE GO. WE MIGHT WIN FIRST PRIZE OF TWENTY-FIVE DOLLARS!

BINGO

OH, BOY! WHAT A KICK THAT WAS! YES, SIR!! NOW, I THINK I'LL TAKE IN A SIDESHOW!

EXIT

ROLLER COASTER

WHEN I WAS A KID, I USED TO BE NUTS ABOUT FREAK SHOWS — THE BEARDED LADY, THE TWO-HEADED CALF ... WELL, WHO IN —

WELL, IF IT ISN'T JERRY! JERRY WOTTS! I HAVEN'T SEEN YOU IN YEARS!

HELLO, STEVE, I THOUGHT YOU WERE IN STIR. WE DON'T WANT ANY EX-CONS AROUND HERE.

AND A FEW FEET AWAY, AT THE BINGO CONCESSION.

TWENTY-EIGHT! NUMBER TWENTY-EIGHT!

GEE, MISS TESS, YOU ONLY NEED A FOURTEEN TO WIN THE TWENTY-FIVE DOLLARS!

SCENE: THE FREAKS' CONCESSION AT OCEAN PARK.

LISTEN, DUKE. YOUR KIND ISN'T WANTED AROUND HERE. NOW, GET OUT OF HERE—AND STAY OUT!

AND AS FOR YOU, STEVE, I'M GIVING YOU A TEMPORARY JOB TAKING TICKETS FOR ME — BUT REMEMBER, NO MONKEY-SHINES!

I'M CERTAINLY GRATEFUL TO YOU, JERRY. BUT, INCIDENTALLY WHO WAS THAT FELLOW YOU WERE JUST TALKING TO?

HE'S A NO-GOOD DIP AND PICK-POCKET WHO USED TO HANG AROUND HERE. WHY?

NOTHING, ONLY HE DISCARDED THAT WOMAN'S PURSE BEHIND THIS CANVAS WHILE HE WAS TALKING TO YOU.

SO YOU WON TWENTY-FIVE DOLLARS IN THE BINGO GAME AND THEN HAD YOUR PURSE SNATCHED, EH? OH, BOY!

OH, I KNOW! WE'RE SUPPOSED TO BE SMART LIKE YOU. I KNOW! I GUESS WE'RE A COUPLE OF DOPES, MISS TESS!

WHAT? YOU SAY THAT FELLOW, DUKE, DUMPED THIS PURSE IN HERE?

YEAH! I SAW HIM WHILE I WAS WASHING ME FACE!

LISTEN, THERE WON'T BE ANYTHING DOING HERE TILL TWO O'CLOCK. GO TO LUNCH WHILE I FIND THAT GUY, DUKE!

FREAK TICKE

THAT DIRTY PICKPOCKET! SNATCHES A PURSE, THEN DIVES INTO MY PLACE TO REMOVE THE DOUGH! WHY, TH—! AH! THERE HE IS!

MEANWHILE, AT THE FRONT GATE OF THE PARK.

HERE'S THE WAY WE'LL WORK IT. YOU TWO SIT DOWN AT THE BINGO GAME AND PLAY. I'LL STAND CLOSE BY AND LOOK OVER THE CROWD OF KIBITZERS. WE MAY FIND YOUR THUG!

JUST A MINUTE, DUKE! I GOT YOU BEFORE YOU GOT AWAY, EH?

WH—?

WHAT PURSE? WHAT DO YOU MEAN?

THIS PURSE. YOU KNOW WHICH PURSE! YOU SNATCHED IT, THEN DUMPED IT IN MY PLACE AFTER CLEANING IT OUT!

I'M TURNING YOU OVER TO THE PARK POLICE, YOU SNEAKING LITTLE DOG! THIS PARK IS SICK AND TIRED OF FOOLING WITH YOU GUYS.

HEY! LET'S GO INTO THE FREAK SHOW BEFORE WE PLAY BINGO!

THE SIDE SHOWS ARE ALL CLOSED TILL TWO O'CLOCK, JUNIOR.

I WONDER WHOSE PURSE IT WAS THAT GUY SNATCHED. HM! I'M GLAD I'M NOT MIXED UP IN IT!

YOU'RE GOING TO THE COPS AND I'M NOT KIDDIN'! PURSE SNATCHERS AREN'T TOLERATED IN THIS PARK!

OH, YEAH!

STOP THAT MAN!

YI!!

EEK!

HELP!

OKAY—START YOUR BINGO GAME. I'LL STROLL AROUND AND SEE IF I CAN GET A LINE ON YOUR PURSE SNATCHER!

OKAY, DICK!

WELL, I LOST DUKE—BUT I'VE GOT THE PURSE. HM—I WONDER WHOSE IT IS?

"TESS TRUEHEART," HM? NEVER HEARD OF HER.

I'LL KEEP THE PURSE HERE A FEW DAYS. THAT GUY, DUKE, MAY SHOW UP AGAIN AND—WHEN I TURN HIM OVER TO THE COPS, I WANT TO TURN OVER THE EVIDENCE WITH HIM.

I THINK GETTING A LINE ON YOUR PURSE SNATCHER IS OUT OF THE QUESTION HERE, TESS. HOW ARE YOU DOING?

THIS IS OUR FOURTH GAME, NO WINS!

TRACY, THE FREAK SHOW OPENS IN TEN MINUTES. LET'S GO THERE!

WELL, I'M BACK FROM LUNCH, JERRY!

GOOD! WE OPEN IN FIVE MINUTES!

I'LL GET OUT FRONT WITH THE MEGAPHONE. YOU TAKE OVER HERE.

OKIE-DOKE!

AS STEVE TOSSES HIS HAT ONTO THE SHELF ABOVE HIS HEAD, IT LANDS ON TOP OF TESS' STOLEN POCKETBOOK.

HOT DOG! THE FREAKS! LET'S GO!

THE MOLE

92

THE MOLE

THE MOLE

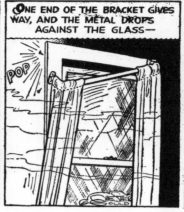

THE MOLE

THE MOLE

THE MOLE

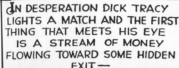

THE MOLE

IN DESPERATION DICK TRACY LIGHTS A MATCH AND THE FIRST THING THAT MEETS HIS EYE IS A STREAM OF MONEY FLOWING TOWARD SOME HIDDEN EXIT—

IT'S AN OUTLET— I'M SAVED!

GUIDED TO SAFETY BY A FLOW OF **MONEY!** THE MOLE'S MONEY!

I SAW THE STREAM OF MONEY FLOWING TOWARD AN EXIT. I FOLLOWED IT!

FOR THE POLICE FUND!

THE MOLE'S STILL UNDER-GROUND.. THERE WAS A CAVE-IN. WE BECAME SEPARATED.

MOLE DIG HIS WAY OUT! EASY FOR MOLE! --COME UP JUST BACK OF FENCE!

NOW, LET ME FIGURE ABOUT WHERE HE'D BE. WE'VE GOT TO GET HIM OUT OF THERE. GET YOUR SHOVELS!

MY FIGURING WOULD PUT THE MOLE'S LOCATION RIGHT ABOUT HERE!

DRIVE THAT PIECE OF PIPE DOWN FIRST SO HE CAN GET SOME FRESH AIR UNTIL WE DIG HIM OUT.

MOLE NOT FAR FROM SURFACE! HAVE TO WORK FAST— OXYGEN ALMOST EXHAUSTED.

LITTLE DOES THE MOLE SUSPECT IT, BUT DIRECTLY IN HIS PATH STANDS A WOODEN FENCE POST -A SIMPLE ARTICLE THAT MAY CAUSE HIM A LOT OF TROUBLE.

WE MUST HAVE MISSED THE TUNNEL ENTIRELY. THE PIPE'S STILL DRIVING VERY HARD!

TAP IT WHILE I LISTEN. WE'LL SEE IF WE CAN GET ANY SIGNALS!

WHAT'S UP?

I'D SWEAR I SAW THAT FENCE POST MOVE!

106

THE MOLE

B. B. EYES

1942

OH, THIS IS TERRIBLE! HORRIBLE! JACQUES IS --- ---DEAD!

YOUNG LADY, I HOPE YOU REALIZE I HAD TO USE MY GUN TO SAVE YOUR LIFE!

COME ALONG! WE'LL ALL HAVE TO TESTIFY AT THE CORONER'S HEARING!

MUST HAVE BEEN A SHOOTING IN THE OLD BIRD CLUB!

YEAH— MUST HAVE BEEN!

WELL, THAT WRITES 'THE FINAL CHAPTER TO JACQUES' CAREER!

IS IT ALL OVER?

PERHAPS EVERYTHING HAS WORKED OUT FOR THE BEST!

YOU TWO PROBABLY WANT TO SPEND A QUIET EVENING AT HOME, BEA. SUPPOSE I STEP OUT AT HEAD-QUARTERS AND WE'LL CONSIDER THIS CASE CLOSED!

WAIT! STOP THE CAR!

THAT'S "SAILOR" KELLY IN THE OTHER CAR. HE'S GOING TO COLLABORATE WITH ME ON THE INTERIOR COLOR SCHEME FOR MY NEW BIRD CLUB!

DOESN'T IT MAKE YOU PROUD, "SAILOR," TO KNOW THAT WHEN THE BIRD CLUB OPENS AGAIN, I'LL BE THE OWNER AND YOU'LL BE THE MANAGER!

LOOK! THIS IS THE NEW TYPE OF UPHOLSTERY, DEBBY! AND I'VE ORDERED THIRTY NEW TABLES.

I'VE GOT IN PART OF THE NEW BAR STOCK AND—

WELL, WHAT ARE WE WAITING FOR?

—AND WHAT DO YOU SAY WE THROW OUT ALL THE OLD FURNITURE!

BANG!

WE'LL JUST STAND HERE AND WAIT. I DON'T LIKE THE LOOKS OF THIS, CLANCY!

DO YOU MEAN THAT DIZZY DAME IS GOING TO REOPEN THIS PLACE?

OUT WITH THE OLD— IN WITH THE NEW! YOWEE!

THE JUNK MAN WON'T HAVE TO WALK FAR FOR THIS OLD FURNITURE, EH, DEBBY?

OKAY, GO IN AND GET 'EM, CLANCY. WE'LL TEACH THAT LITTLE DAME A LESSON!

YES, UNDER ARREST —FOR DISTURBING THE PEACE!

UNDER ARREST?? HOW DARE YOU?

111

B.B. EYES

LOCK 'EM UP — DO **ANYTHING**. I DON'T CARE!

I'M WASHING MY HANDS OF THIS WHOLE THORNDIKE FAMILY. THEY'RE **NUTS**!

THIRTY MINUTES LATER —
THEY'RE A BUNCH OF UNPRINCIPLED, SELFISH, IMMORAL SCREWBALLS!

MR. TRACY!
SIT DOWN! I'VE GOT A FEW THINGS TO **TELL** YOU! THEN I'M PARTING COMPANY WITH YOU AND YOUR NIECE, FOREVER!

YES, CHIEF, THAT'S WHAT I SAID. TRACY HAS JUST **BROKEN HIS LEG**!

HE WAS LEAVING BEA THORNDIKE'S HOME WHEN HE SLIPPED ON THE ICE.

BUT **FIVE WEEKS**! I CAN'T STAY IN THIS **CRAZY** THORNDIKE HOME FOR **FIVE WEEKS**, DOC!
YOU'LL **HAVE** TO!

YOU'LL LIKE IT HERE, MR TRACY. I'LL PLAN A PARTY FOR YOU. BY THE WAY, THE JUDGE JUST FINED "SAILOR" AND ME TEN DOLLARS. DO YOU THINK THAT WAS HIGH?
DOC! SEE WHAT I MEAN?

YES — HE'S UPSTAIRS, GENTLEMEN. COME THIS WAY!

WE PLAN TO OPEN THE BIRD CLUB TOMORROW NIGHT. IT WILL BE ONE OF THE SEASON'S MOST GALA EVENTS. **ALL** SOCIETY WILL BE THERE!
HO HUM!

HELLO, DICK!
THOUGHT WE'D DROP AROUND!
THE RESCUE SQUAD!

ACROSS THE STREET — THAT'S THE THORNDIKE HOME. THE PAPERS SAY HE'LL HAVE TO STAY THERE FIVE WEEKS!
FIVE WEEKS, EH? HM!
WHO ARE THESE MEN — YES, WHO?

THAT'S FINAL, TRACY. I HAD QUITE A TALK WITH THE DOCTOR. YOUR FRACTURE IS SO BAD — HE WILL **NOT** LET YOU MOVE, SO YOU MIGHT AS WELL QUIT FRETTING!

AND NOW, LADIES AND GENTLEMEN, WE TAKE YOU TO THE NEW BIRD CLUB — WHERE YOUR MISTRESS OF CEREMONIES WILL BE DEBBY THORNDIKE!
TURN THAT THING OFF!

NICE LOOKING CROWD SHE'S GOT FOR OPENING NIGHT!
GRAND OPENING

YEAH! LET'S MUSCLE IN. I'D LIKE TO TAKE A LOOK AT THAT DAME!
OKAY! WE **KNOW** THE FLATFOOT WON'T BE THERE!

B.B. EYES

114

B. B. EYES

116

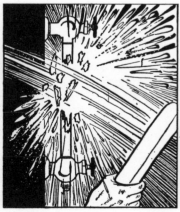

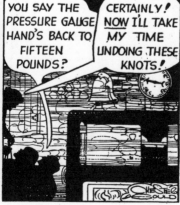

WE'VE GOT A LITTLE HOT WATER TO WADE AROUND IN, BUT THE DANGER IS ALL GONE!

THE STEAM'S CLEARING UP, TOO!

NOW, IF YOU GIRLS JUST GIVE ME A HAND, I THINK I CAN WALK OUT OKAY!

WHAT A LIFE-SAVER, WHEN YOU THOUGHT OF BREAKING THAT WATER GAUGE, BEA!

AN EMERGENCY SOMETIMES BRINGS BACK FORGOTTEN KNOWLEDGE!

AND FOUR BLOCKS AWAY—

YEAH— SOMETHING WENT WRONG. TURN THIS BUGGY AROUND!

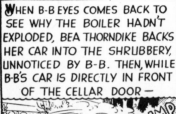

WHEN B-B EYES COMES BACK TO SEE WHY THE BOILER HADN'T EXPLODED, BEA THORNDIKE BACKS HER CAR INTO THE SHRUBBERY, UNNOTICED BY B-B. THEN, WHILE B-B'S CAR IS DIRECTLY IN FRONT OF THE CELLAR DOOR—

BUMP

THEY'RE PRISONERS! THEY CAN'T OPEN THE DOORS OF THEIR CAR!

WE'VE CAPTURED THEM!

BUT I TELL YOU, B-B, WE CAN'T GET OUT!

LET'S BREAK THROUGH THE WINDSHIELD.

WON'T DO ANY GOOD. THE WINDSHIELD IS RIGHT AGAINST THE TOP OF THE BASEMENT DOOR!

WE CAN'T OPEN THE DOORS - AND THE WINDSHIELD IS BLOCKED OFF. MAYBE WE CAN MAKE A GET-AWAY THROUGH THE REAR WINDOW?

THEY'RE MAKING THOSE TOO SMALL THESE DAYS. WE COULDN'T CRAWL THROUGH!

BEA, HELP ME OUT, WILL YOU?

WHAT? NO! NO! DICK!

HE'LL SHOOT YOU RIGHT THROUGH HIS CAR WINDOW. HE'LL KILL YOU!

I DON'T THINK SO, BEA!

EASY, B-B EYES! YOU'LL JUST HAVE A MURDER CHARGE ON YOUR HANDS IN ADDITION TO EVERYTHING ELSE. PUT IT AWAY, I WANT TO TALK TO YOU!

PUT IT AWAY, B-B. YOU'LL JUST HAVE MORE TROUBLE ON YOUR HANDS IF YOU SHOOT ME!

I ADVISE YOU TO SIT QUIETLY IN THERE AND RELAX UNTIL THE SQUAD CAR ARRIVES. THEY'LL PULL YOUR CAR BACK AND TAKE YOU OUT!

I'M NOT ARMED BUT I'LL STAY HERE ANYWAY AND KEEP AN EYE ON THEM WHILE YOU GO AFTER THE POLICE, BEA!

WE'LL LEAVE THIS CAR CUSHION FOR YOU, MR. TRACY!

OKAY! WELL, GET GOING, GIRLS!

AS TRACY AWAITS THE RETURN OF BEA THORNDIKE AND THE POLICE —

B. B. EYES

I TALKED THE DOC INTO TAKING OFF THE CAST AND I BELIEVE IF I USE THIS CANE I CAN HOBBLE AROUND!

WELL, TAKE IT EASY, TRACY!

DOESN'T IT SEEM STRANGE TO YOU THAT IN TIMES LIKE THESE, B-B'S CAR SHOULD HAVE BRAND NEW TIRES??

THE SERIAL NUMBERS HAVE BEEN GROUND OFF. THEY'RE HOT TIRES, ALL RIGHT, TRACY!

WE MAY BE ABLE TO GET SOMEWHERE YET!

WHAT DO YOU MEAN, TRACY?

IF WE CAN JUST FIND OUT WHO'S BOOTLEGGING TIRES WE MAY BE ABLE TO GET A LINE ON B-B!

IN AN ATTEMPT TO LOCATE B-B EYES, TRACY DECIDES TO FIND THE SOURCE OF THE BOOTLEG TIRES FOUND ON B-B'S CAR—

TURN IN HERE, PAT. WE MIGHT AS WELL START WITH THIS PLACE!

SAY, BUD, CONFIDENTIALLY, WHERE CAN A FELLOW PICK UP-ER- A COUPLE OF TIRES WITHOUT A PRIORITIES ORDER?-ER-YOU KNOW- A BOOTLEG TIRE?

LISTEN, BROTHER- YOU SAY THAT AGAIN AND I'LL CALL A COP. YOU'RE TALKING ABOUT BREAKING THE LAW!

WELL, NOW, WAIT A MINUTE!

I'M GOING TO TAKE YOUR NUMBER, BRIGHT EYES! THERE'S A WAR ON AND IT'S FELLOWS LIKE YOU WE'VE GOT TO KEEP OUR EYES ON!

HM!

ONE OF THE BOYS GOT IT FROM THE GRAPEVINE THAT A FELLOW NAMED "JUKE" IS THE GO-BETWEEN FOR THE TIRE BOYS. HE HANGS OUT IN THAT OLD GARAGE!

THANKS, O'MALLEY!

HELLO, JUKE!

I'M MR. JAMES. I WANT A COUPLE OF TIRES!

THERE'S THE PRICE LIST. LOOK IT OVER AND PAY ME! I'LL TELL YOU WHERE YOU CAN PICK UP THE TIRES.

BUT I DON'T SEE ANY TIRES HERE-WHERE ARE THEY?

IF YOU WANT THE TIRES I CAN GET THEM. IF YOU WANT TO ASK SILLY QUESTIONS GET OUT!

I'VE MARKED THE SIZE TIRES I WANT THERE ON THE PRICE LIST, AND HERE IS THE THIRTY BUCKS!

EXCUSE ME A MOMENT!

TAKE THIS PRICE LIST OVER TO THE BOYS FOR A CHECK-UP OF THE FINGERPRINTS!

HALF HOUR LATER-

BOSS! IT'S A GOOD THING WE'RE USING A FINGERPRINT SYSTEM TO CHECK-UP ON OUR NEW CUSTOMERS. WHO DO YOU THINK OUR LATEST ONE IS?

STILL LATER —

THEY GAVE ME THIS ADDRESS, O'MALLEY, AND SAID IF I'D SEND A MAN OVER THERE HE COULD PICK UP THE TIRES!

HOT DOG! SEND ME, TRACY, I'M DYING TO MEET THOSE TIRE 'LEGGERS!

120

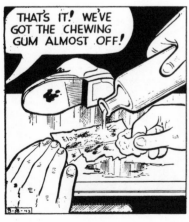

B.B. EYES

FIRST THING WE MUST DO IS LOCATE ELAY HARDWARE COMPANY, TWENTY SOUTH END STREET, SHOWN ON THE PAPER STUCK TO O'MALLEY'S SHOE!

SOUTH END STREET IS NO DAZZLING BOULEVARD, PAT!

YOU SAID IT, TRACY! *LOOK!*

THERE'S THE PLACE! NUMBER TWENTY. IT'S A DINGY LOOKING DUMP!

BUT THE ELAY HARDWARE IS A BIG OUTFIT. WHAT WOULD THEY BE DOING WITH THAT?

DON'T LOOK NOW, BUT ISN'T THAT A SQUAD CAR?

I CALLED ELAY HARDWARE'S MAIN OFFICE AND THEY SAID THEY MOVED FROM THAT SOUTH END ADDRESS **TWELVE** YEARS AGO!

THEY MUST HAVE LEFT SOME OF THEIR OLD BILL HEADS BEHIND WHEN THEY MOVED.

YES, IT WAS ONE OF THEM THAT WAS STUCK TO O'MALLEY'S SHOE! WELL, LET'S TAKE MY CAR TODAY, PAT!

LATER

B-B EYES, THE BOYS IN THE FRONT OFFICE ARE A LITTLE WORRIED. THEY WANT TO TALK TO YOU!

WELL, WHAT DO YOU MUGS WANT? WHAT'S GOT YOU WORRIED?

JUST SIT DOWN QUIETLY, B-B, AND WATCH THAT WOOD FENCE ACROSS THE STREET!

I THOUGHT I SAW SOMEONE MOVING AROUND IN THERE, TRACY!

YES, THERE ARE TWO—MAYBE THREE!

YOU'RE RIGHT, BOYS, WE'RE BEING WATCHED!

SHALL I TURN OFF THE LIGHT, B-B?

NO, NOT YET!

STAY IN HERE FIVE MINUTES, THEN DOUSE THE LIGHT AND COME BACK INTO THE GARAGE!

BOYS, I WANT EACH OF YOU TO GRAB ONE OF THESE TWO-BY-FOURS AND STAND RIGHT BACK OF THAT STACK OF TIRES!

WHAT'S UP, B-B EYES?

JUST AS I FIGURED. THE FLATFOOT USED HIS SKELETON KEY TO ENTER THE "OFFICE" AFTER WE LEFT—AND THEN FOLLOWED US BACK HERE.

ARE YOU DOWN THERE UNDER THE NICE SOFT TIRES, MR. TRACY? HMMM???

WHY, **LOOK**, BOYS! HE EVEN HAD HIS GUN READY. HE MUST HAVE BEEN GOING TO **SHOOT** SOMEBODY!

BUT YOU CAN'T LEAVE THEM BACK THERE VERY LONG, B-B EYES. THEY'LL **SMOTHER** UNDER THOSE TIRES!

LET 'EM SMOTHER FOR A FEW MINUTES WHILE WE FIGURE OUT WHAT TO DO NEXT.

B.B. EYES

B.B. EYES

LET 'ER GO!

HE'S GOING TO DUMP. **WE'LL BE TOO LATE!**

GEARS CLASH, CHAINS JANGLE AS THREE BUCKETS OPEN TO DISGORGE THEIR BURDEN—

MUD, WATER, STONES, CANS — AND, YES—EVEN A DILAPIDATED TIRE SETTLE NOISLESSLY DOWN INTO THE DARK DEPTHS OF THE BAY, ACCOMPANIED BY B-B EYES.

DON'T DUMP THE SCOW! CAN YOU HEAR ME? DON'T DUMP THE SCOW??? WHY, THE SCOW'S ALREADY DUMPED!

AS B-B EYES AND THE DEBRIS SETTLE A STRANGE THING HAPPENS—

THE MAN WHO <u>DEALT</u> IN STOLEN TIRES FINDS HIMSELF, IN HIS FINAL FATEFUL MOMENTS, IMPRISONED IN AN ABANDONED CASING—

WE'RE <u>TOO LATE</u>!

WHAT DO YOU MEAN, THERE WAS A MAN IN THAT MUD?

AN ESCAPED PRISONER-- LEAPED FROM THE BRIDGE! HE MAY HAVE BEEN DEAD BEFORE THEY DUMPED!

SUPPOSE WE CIRCLE THE SCOW AND WATCH THE WATER FOR ANY SIGNS! OKAY, THERE MIGHT BE A CHANCE!

88 KEYES

1943

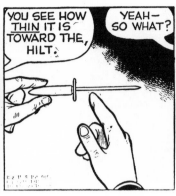

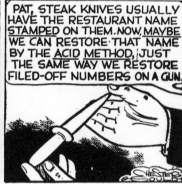

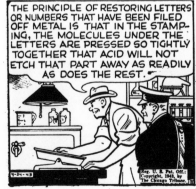

88 KEYES

TAKING THE GRINDING WHEEL FROM THE PIANO TUNER'S BAG, DICK TRACY AND PAT PATTON DEPART FOR HEADQUARTERS—

HOW DOES THIS GRINDING WHEEL TIE IN, TRACY?

JUST THIS WAY, PAT: IN THE MANUFACTURING OF THE DAGGER.

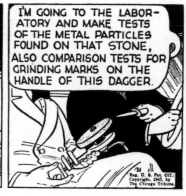

I'M GOING TO THE LABORATORY AND MAKE TESTS OF THE METAL PARTICLES FOUND ON THAT STONE, ALSO COMPARISON TESTS FOR GRINDING MARKS ON THE HANDLE OF THIS DAGGER.

WHAT I WANT YOU TO DO IS GET OUT AT THE NEXT CORNER AND GO BACK TO THE DOVE CLUB. SHADOW THAT PIANO TUNER TILL YOU HEAR FROM ME.

WHAT DO YOU FIND, NOLAN?

H'M!

THERE'S NO QUESTION ABOUT IT, TRACY. THE METAL PARTICLES FOUND ON THIS GRINDING WHEEL CAME OFF THAT STEAK KNIFE! SAME METAL!

PAT'S ON THE PHONE. HE WANTS TO KNOW IF YOU HAVE ANY WORD FOR HIM.

I WAS JUST GOING TO CALL YOU, PAT. ARREST OUR PIANO TUNER FRIEND AND BRING HIM IN IMMEDIATELY. IN HANDCUFFS!

PUT DOWN THAT PHONE! YOU'LL NOT CALL TUNER.

YOU WILL SNEAK INTO THE ROOM AND EAVESDROP WHILE I'M TALKING TO THE RICH WIDOW, EH?

BUT YOU'RE IN LOVE WITH HER—AND HER INSURANCE MONEY. YOU'VE DOUBLE-CROSSED TUNER AND ME.

CERTAINLY, I DOUBLE-CROSSED YOU. AND THE WIDOW AND I ARE GOING TO RUN AWAY, AH, HA, HA! WITH 200 GRAND.

NOW JUST SIGN THESE PAPERS, MRS. HELMET. THEY SHOW RECEIPT OF PAYMENT FOR THE FULL AMOUNT OF YOUR HUSBAND'S INSURANCE POLICIES.

THERE YOU ARE. A CHECK FOR 200 THOUSAND DOLLARS. WOULD YOU LIKE TO DEPOSIT IT OR—

I WOULD LIKE THE CASH, PLEASE.

MEANWHILE—

SHE'S DEAD!

STONE DEAD!

A CORPSE ON MY HANDS. WHAT SHOULD I DO? THE BODY! WHERE CAN I PUT IT? HUH??

135

88 KEYES

YES, TUNER, WE FOUND THE GIRL SINGER TUCKED AWAY IN THE PIANO.

WHY THAT DIRTY—

5-10-43

NOW DON'T YOU THINK YOU OUGHT TO TALK?

OKAY! I WILL TALK.

Reg. U. S. Pat. Off. Copyright, 1943, by The Chicago Tribune.

88 KEYES, THE GIRL SINGER AND I MURDERED A. B. HELMET FOR THREE THOUSAND DOLLARS, AT THE REQUEST OF HELMET'S WIFE.

I DID THE ACTUAL STABBING DURING A SINGING NUMBER WHILE THE HOUSE LIGHTS WERE OFF. I MADE THE DAGGER FROM A STEAK KNIFE BUT I DIDN'T KNOW THAT 88 KEYES WAS—

YES, GO ON.

AS I SAID, THE SINGER AND I CONSPIRED WITH 88 TO MURDER A. B. HELMET FOR A GRAND APIECE. BUT WE DIDN'T KNOW 88 HAD BEEN IN LOVE WITH MRS. HELMET YEARS AGO.

IN OTHER WORDS 88 KEYES WANTED MRS. HELMET AND HER MONEY FOR HIMSELF.

YEAH. AND THE GIRL AND I WERE DOPES ENOUGH TO GO ALONG WITH HIM.

5-11-43

Reg. U. S. Pat. Off. Copyright, 1943, by The Chicago Tribune.

WAS THAT THE FIRST MURDER YOU THREE HAD EVER COMMITTED —FOR MONEY?

NO. IT WAS THE FOURTH.

MEANWHILE, SPEEDING MANY MILES WESTWARD.

THERE, 88, DEAR, SEE HOW I TRUST YOU? YOU HAVE MY INSURANCE MONEY AND YOU HAVE ME.

YEAH

SAY, MISTER, YOUR TANK WAS EMPTY. IT HELD EXACTLY 23 GALLONS. THAT'LL BE 6 COUPONS AND FOUR SIXTY.

5-12-43

THERE YOU ARE OLD BOY. KEEP THE CHANGE.

YES, SIR, 23 GALLONS. SIX COUPONS.

Reg. U. S. Pat. Off. Copyright, 1943, by The Chicago Tribune.

HEY! THERE'S ONLY ONE COUPON HERE. HEY YOU!! WELL I'LL BE ～☆!!

AND IN YOUR OPINION, TUNER, 88 KEYES' LOVE FOR MRS. HELMET IS NOT VERY DEEP, EH?

HAH! AS SOON AS HE GETS HIS HANDS ON THAT INSURANCE MONEY SHE COLLECTED HE'LL LEAVE HER OR —KILL HER.

HONEY, DON'T YOU THINK WE OUGHT TO STOP SOMEWHERE? WE'VE BEEN DRIVING FOR TWO DAYS.

WE'LL KEEP DRIVING TILL NIGHTFALL.

Reg. U. S. Pat. Off. Copyright, 1943, by The Chicago Tribune.

THEN, I'LL GET OUT MY PORTABLE PHONOGRAPH AND PLAY SOME OF YOUR RECORDINGS, DARLING.

NIGHT AND DAY

HM! ASLEEP. SHE'S EXHAUSTED! DEAD TO THE WORLD.

136

TWO DAYS WITHOUT SLEEP. SHE'S EXHAUSTED.

IT'S THE WESTERN LIMITED. WITH THIS PHONOGRAPH GOING SHE'LL NEVER HEAR IT.

I'LL SET THE PICK-UP BACK AT THE BEGINNING AGAIN.

I'VE GOT THE 200 GRAND IN MY POCKET, WHAT HAVE I GOT TO LOSE?

TOOT

SCREECH

THEY MUST BE DOING NINETY MILES AN HOUR. THEY CAN'T STOP.

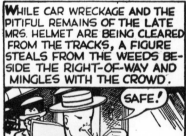

WHILE CAR WRECKAGE AND THE PITIFUL REMAINS OF THE LATE MRS. HELMET ARE BEING CLEARED FROM THE TRACKS, A FIGURE STEALS FROM THE WEEDS BESIDE THE RIGHT-OF-WAY AND MINGLES WITH THE CROWD.

SAFE!

—AND HEADED RIGHT BACK TO THE CITY. I'LL SPEND THE NIGHT HERE IN THE SMOKER.

LICENSE CHECK-UP SHOWS IT WAS ISSUED TO ONE A.B. HELMET IN THE CITY.

GET THE BODY IN THE WAGON BOYS.

THIS IS A FUNNY SET UP— A PHONOGRAPH AND RECORDS. —AND HER POSITION ON THE SEAT WOULD INDICATE SHE WASN'T EVEN BEHIND THE WHEEL.

THE CRASH HAPPENED NEAR WELLMAN.

DON'T YOU **SEE**, TRACY, IT'S JUST LIKE WE PREDICTED.

88 KEYES GOT THE WIDOW'S MONEY AND **DUMPED HER.**

GET ME STATE POLICE HEADQUARTERS AT WELLMAN.

ONE OF THE BOYS FOUND SOME FOOT PRINTS COMING OUT OF THAT GRASS, CHIEF.

WAIT FELLOWS! THAT'S OUR CALL COMING IN ON THE SHORT WAVE.

BUT I'VE FOLLOWED ALL DE JIVE BANDS. I SEEN 'EM **ALL** - WHEN DEY PLAYED DE PALACE. AND I SAY DAT MAN IS 88 KEYES!

SHO NUFF!

88 KEYES

FOOTPRINTS LEAD FROM THAT MARSHY GRASS UP ON TO THE CRUSHED ROCK OF THE ROAD BED.

H'M COULDN'T HAVE BEEN ANY OF THE TRAIN PASSENGERS BECAUSE THE TRAIN STOPPED DOWN THERE.

THE HEAVY TOE INDENTURE, AND SLIGHT HEEL MARKS SHOW THE PARTY WAS RUNNING. WE'D BETTER MAKE SOME PLASTER CASTS OF THEM.

BEING AN ARDENT FOLLOWER OF YOUR HOT JIVE, MR. 88 KEYES, I SHO' WOULD BE HONORED WITH YO' AUTOGRAPH.

I'M SORRY, GEORGE, BUT YOU'VE GOT THE WRONG MAN. MY NAME'S JEFFERIES - S.A. JEFFERIES.

OH, I BEG YOUR PARDON, SUH! BUT YO' CERTAINLY DO LOOK LIKE 88.

YOU BIG BOOB! I TOL' YOU DAT WASN'T NO 88 KEYES.

AND ME A JIVE AUTHORITY! I CAN'T GET OVER IT.

GOTTA WATCH THESE BABIES. THEY'RE SMARTER THAN THE COPPERS. HM? WONDER WHAT TOWN THIS IS?

HERE YOU ARE BUTCH - THE PAWNEE PAPERS.

HM! SOUNDS LOGICAL! WELLMAN POLICE SAY FOOT PRINTS INDICATE 88 MAY HAVE BOARDED THE SAME TRAIN THAT KILLED THE WIDOW.

NOW THAT'S NUTS! OH THOSE SMALL TOWN

EVENING PAPERS. ORCHESTRA LEADER SOUGHT IN TRAIN CRASH!

88 KEYES SOUGHT AFTER CRASH

I'VE GOT TO KEEP MOVING TOWARD THE REAR OF THE TRAIN WHILE I FIGURE OUT WHAT TO DO. THAT NEWSIE WILL WORK HIS WAY BACK FROM THE SMOKER.

THIS IS THE CLUB CAR - THE END OF THE TRAIN. HE'LL BE BACK HERE IN A MATTER OF MINUTES.

OKAY! SO I'M IN THE WASH ROOM, NOW WHAT??

EVENING PAPER. ORCHESTRA LEADER SOUGHT IN MURDER.

I'VE GOT TO STAY IN THIS WASH ROOM TILL WE GET INTO THE STATION.

THERE'S A FLASH COMING IN OVER THE RADIO ON THAT 88 KEYES' CASE NOW.

LET'S LISTEN.

JACKSON! WHAT DID I TELL YOU! IT WAS HIM! I WAS RIGHT.

BROTHER. YOU WAS DIGGING IN DE GROOVE AND I DOUBTED YOU. 88 KEYES IS HERE. ON DIS TRAIN.

88 KEYES

While smoke from an incoming train on track one suddenly rolls between 88 Keyes and Dick Tracy—the detective decides to rush the killer and tackle him hand-to-hand.

We can't fire at 88 on account of the **smoke**.

Ye gods! This smoke is thicker than I thought. And it's full of **cinders**.

Choked—and startled at his sudden predicament, Tracy falters, his foot misses the coping, and—

My foot slipped on that coping! That smoke was blinding.

CRASH

While 88 Keyes, taking advantage of the smoke screen, crosses the next roof and reaches a window.

Meanwhile, the glass in the trainshed roof, being reinforced with chicken wire, breaks the detective's fall and holds him fast—a captive.

Well, that's the fourth bus full of farmhands we've shipped out today.

EMPLOYMENT AGENCY

COUNTRY BUS LINES

When I ducked into that employment bureau, I never dreamed I'd be signing up for a farm job.

Okay—so we trailed him through that open window and down the stairway after getting you off the trainshed roof. Now what?

I hope they place me on a hog raising farm. I hate to milk cows. What about you, brother?

I'll take anything, just so it's IN THE COUNTRY.

Well, here we are, boys.

U.S. EMPLOYMENT BUREAU

COUNTY BUS LIN

Now, we'll assign you men to farms where help is needed most. If you have any complaints, report to this office.

Smith, you'll go to the George Wheaten farm. Here's Mr. Wheaten now.

Glad to know you, Pop. Where's this farm of yours?

Hm! Experienced farmhand, eh??

140

WHILE 88 KEYES IS TEARING UP HIS IDENTIFICATION CARDS, FRAGMENTS FROM ONE CARD FALL INTO A MILK CAN. BUT BEFORE HE CAN RETRIEVE THEM, THE DOOR OPENS.

OKAY, JUNIOR. I'LL GO.

DAD WANTS YOU IN THE DAIRY BARN. WANTS YOU TO THROW DOWN COW FEED.

THE FARMER'S SON PLACES A MILK STRAINER OVER AN EMPTY CAN AND—

—IN LESS TIME THAN IT TAKES TO SAY IT, ONE OF 88 KEYES' IDENTIFICATION CARDS BECOMES PART AND PARCEL OF A CAN OF GRADE A MILK.

THE CAN WITH THE CARD

SCENE: MILK DEPOT OF THE PERFECT MILK CO.

HEY, DOC, PUT A REJECT TICKET ON THAT CAN OF OLD MAN WHEATEN'S MILK.

WHAT'S THE MATTER WITH IT, JOE?

FOREIGN MATTER. LOOKS LIKE PIECES OF PAPER.

YOU MEAN PIECES OF CARDBOARD. HM?? LOOKS LIKE FRAGMENTS OF A BUSINESS CARD.

WHAT DOES IT SAY ON IT?

YEAH. THIS IS DOC WYLIE OF THE PERFECT MILK CO. I'VE READ ABOUT THIS 88 KEYES, THE KILLER—AND I HAVE HIS UNION CARD IN FRONT OF ME.

SAY **NOTHING** TO ANYONE! PAT PATTON AND I WILL BE RIGHT OUT. AND THANKS, DOC.

IT'S FUNNY THEY'D REJECT A CAN OF MILK JUST BECAUSE THERE WERE TWO LITTLE PIECES OF PAPER IN IT.

WHAT DOES IT SAY ON THEM, SON?

ALL I CAN MAKE OUT IS PART OF A SIGNATURE AND "—IANS UNION."

HERE WE ARE, PAT.

PERFECT MILK CO.

MILK.

GLAD TO KNOW YOU, DOC. WYLIE. LET'S HEAR WHAT YOU KNOW ABOUT THIS 88 KEYES.

WELL, I'VE GOT HIS MUSICIANS UNION CARD RIGHT OVER HERE.

YES, THERE'S 88'S SIGNATURE. HM! THIS WAS FOUND IN A CAN OF MILK, EH?

THE MILK CAME FROM OLD MAN WHEATEN'S FARM. THAT'S ABOUT FOUR MILES NORTH OF TOWN.

YES, I'VE GOT A MAP RIGHT HERE. I CAN SHOW YOU THE LOCATION IN NO TIME.

88 KEYES

YEAH— I'D LIKE A CAP, A SHIRT— AND A PAIR OF TROUSERS FOR MY FOURTEEN YEAR OLD BOY!

YES, SIR. RIGHT THIS WAY.

I HAD TO GUESS AT THE SIZES. BUT GET IN THE BACK SEAT AND START PUTTING THEM ON.

OH, MR. SMITH, WE'RE GOING TO BE SO HAPPY TOGETHER.

COME ON, GET DRESSED —BEFORE A COP CAR PASSES US!

SEE?· YOU'D NEVER GUESS I WAS A GIRL, WOULD YOU?

COME ON, SIT DOWN HERE, NELLIE. WE'VE GOT TO MAKE THE BIG CITY BEFORE MORNING.

OH, I—I LOVE YOU SO, MR. SMITH. I'LL MAKE YOU A GOOD WIFE.

THAT'S GREAT, NELLIE! —ER, BY THE WAY— PULL OUT THOSE GAS COUPONS— I'M TURNING IN HERE.

WHEN 88 KEYES AND NELLIE PULL INTO A GASOLINE STATION FOR GAS, THEY ARE GREETED BY A GOB WHO RECOGNIZES NELLIE.

RED BLUFF, WHAT ARE YOU DOING BACK HOME?

ER—I WAS KICKED OUT FOR SOCKING AN OFFICER. I'M HITCHHIKING BACK HOME TO BARRINGDEL. ER—SO THIS IS YOUR FIANCE, EH, NELLIE?

AHA, HA! HA!

ER-- HR-- HRUMPH!

A DOLLAR EIGHTY CENTS, PLEASE.

NELLIE, THIS FIANCE LOOKS STRANGELY FAMILIAR· TO ME— LET'S SEE-- YEAH, I REMEMBER --AT A NAVY SHOW.

I'M SORRY WE CAN'T GIVE YOU A LIFT BACK HOME, RED, BUT WE'RE GOING IN THE OPPOSITE DIRECTION.

YEAH? MAYBE I DON'T WANT TO GO HOME AFTER ALL—

HEY!—I KNOW YOU NOW! IT JUST CAME TO ME—

ER-EXCUSE US A MINUTE, WILL YOU, NELLIE?

LISTEN—YOU'RE 88 KEYES, THE ORCHESTRA LEADER WHO'S WANTED FOR MURDER—I KNOW—

SH!— SH!

W-WHAT'S IT WORTH TO YOU TO KEEP QUIET, RED? HUH?

CONFIDENTIALLY BETWEEN YOU AND ME, I'M A DESERTER MAYBE WE COULD TEAM UP, EH?

147

88 KEYES

148

FLATTOP

1943–1944

DICK TRACY

YES—HE SAW HIS BROTHER, KIRK, JUST IN TIME. LAFFY IS DEAD.

WHAT'S THAT IN HIS LEFT HAND?

A NEWSPAPER CLIPPING ABOUT THE MAYOR'S RECEPTION FOR KIRK.

THUS, WHILE ONE BROTHER LEAVES THIS WORLD AND A CAREER OF CRIME, THE OTHER BROTHER RETURNS TO THE BATTLEFRONT TO FIGHT FOR HIS COUNTRY AND HUMANITY.

IT'S THAT WAR HERO! GOOD LUCK, BOY!

BUD, WHICH WAY TO THE NOBLE HOTEL?

DICK TRACY

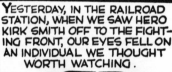

YESTERDAY, IN THE RAILROAD STATION, WHEN WE SAW HERO KIRK SMITH OFF TO THE FIGHTING FRONT, OUR EYES FELL ON AN INDIVIDUAL WE THOUGHT WORTH WATCHING.

NOBLE HOTEL, DRIVER

GOT TO GET A ROOM, THEN CONTACT THIS FELLOW, ED. H'M. FIVE GRAND ISN'T BAD FOR SUCH A SMALL JOB.

H'M. A FUNNY LOOKING EGG.

DICK TRACY

WE HAVEN'T NOTIFIED KIRK OF LAFFY'S DEATH—AND PERHAPS IT'S BEST THAT WAY. HE'LL HAVE A HAPPIER CHRISTMAS.

TESS, IT LOOKS AS THOUGH THIS IS ONE CHRISTMAS WEEK I'LL REALLY HAVE TIME TO GO CHRISTMAS SHOPPING WITH YOU.

REALLY. I CAN HARDLY BELIEVE THAT YOU DON'T HAVE SOME IMPORTANT CASE ON HAND.

YES, GAL, LET'S GO. I'M AS FREE AS THE AIR! NOT A WORRY IN THE WORLD.

MEANWHILE

HELLO. I'M AT THE NOBLE HOTEL AS PER INSTRUCTIONS. WHAT'S THE SETUP FROM HERE ON?

DICK TRACY

IT WON'T REALLY SEEM LIKE CHRISTMAS, DICK, TILL EVERYONE'S SONS AND BROTHERS ARE BACK.

THAT'S RIGHT, TESS.

AND MAY THAT DAY COME SOONER THAN ANY OF US SUSPECT.

WELL, HERE'S THE TRUEHEART MANSION.

★

RAY

DICK! WELL! WELL! IT'S HARD TO BELIEVE YOU'RE REALLY GOING TO SPEND A CHRISTMAS EVE QUIETLY, WITH NO GANGSTERS TO CHASE.

NOW, MOTHER.

AND IN A HOTEL ROOM

WHAT IF IT **IS** CHRISTMAS? I WANT TO GET THIS JOB **DONE** AND **OVER** WITH.

OKAY, HERE'S THE MONEY.

FLATTOP

DICK TRACY

DICK TRACY

DICK TRACY

DICK TRACY

FLATTOP

DICK TRACY

BUT WE'VE **GOT** TO GIVE FLATTOP THE FIFTY THOUSAND. WE CAN'T TAKE A CHANCE ON HIS RELEASING TRACY AND SICKING THE COPPER ON **US**.

OH-H-OH-H! FIFTY THOUSAND!

WHOSE IDEA WAS IT, HIRING THIS FLATTOP, ANYWAY?

IT WAS MINE, **SO WHAT,** YOU FELLOWS AGREED IT WAS A GREAT HUNCH.

STAY AWAY FROM THE WINDOWS, COPPER. WE DON'T WANT YOU TO GET TOO **NOSY**.

I'M GOING DOWN TO THE CORNER FOR A MALTED MILK AND A NEWSPAPER. KEEP YOUR EYES ON HIM.

DICK TRACY

H'M? THERE GOES THAT LITTLE GIRL THAT LIVES IN THE APARTMENT DOWNSTAIRS. SHE'S A CUTE TRICK.

ARE YOU TAKING A BUS, TOO, THIS MORNING?

ER-YES, SIR.

BUS STOP

LET ME INTRODUCE MYSELF. MY NAME'S JONES. I LIVE IN THE APARTMENT ABOVE YOU.

HOW DO YOU DO? MY NAME'S MARGIE.

THERE HE GOES, FLIRTING WITH THE GIRL DOWNSTAIRS. WHY DON'T FELLOWS LIKE HIM **LEAVE DAMES ALONE**?

DICK TRACY

I CAN'T GET OVER IT. THOSE BIG SHOT GUNMEN **ALWAYS** THINK THEY'RE TOPS WITH THE WOMEN.

HE SHOULD STAY AWAY FROM THAT KID DOWNSTAIRS.

SO YOU'RE PLANNING TO JOIN THE **WACS**, EH?

YES, I WANT TO ENTER THE SIGNAL CORPS DIVISION.

WHAT'S THAT STICKING OUT OF YOUR BAG?

OH, THAT? IT'S A TELEGRAPHER'S SENDING KEY. I USE IT IN MY **WAC** TRAINING.

GOSH, YOU'RE A CUTE KID. MAYBE WE COULD GO OUT TO DINNER ONE OF THESE NIGHTS, 'UM?

I'M AFRAID NOT, MR. JONES. YOU SEE, I'M **VERY** BUSY.

DICK TRACY

WELL! DO WE GIVE FLATTOP THE **FIFTY THOUSAND** OR NOT?

IT'S ROBBERY. ABSOLUTE ROBBERY!

SUPPOSE WE **DON'T** PAY HIM AND SUPPOSE FLATTOP **DOES** GIVE THE DETECTIVE OUR NAMES AND TURNS HIM LOOSE. HE CAN'T PROVE ANYTHING.

RIGHT! IT'S HIS WORD AGAINST OURS.

HOW MUCH **LONGER** IS FLATTOP GOING TO **HOLD THIS MUG**? I WANT THE JOB OVER WITH AND I **WANT** MY MONEY.

PIPE DOWN. HERE HE IS, NOW. ASK HIM.

GENTLEMEN! HAVE I TOLD YOU ABOUT THE LITTLE **WAC** DOWNSTAIRS, HUH?

FLATTOP DOESN'T KNOW IT BUT HE'S GOING TO GET AWFULLY SICK OF THAT LITTLE WAC.

DICK TRACY

BUT SHE'S A CUTE KID.

WHO **CARES**? WHAT WE WANT IS TO GET THIS JOB OVER WITH AND GET OUR **MONEY**.

THERE'S NO HURRY. WE'VE GOT THE BIG SHOTS BY THE NECK. LET THEM WORRY. WE'RE AFTER BIG STAKES.

AND IN THE APARTMENT BELOW.

CLICK- CLICK- CLICKETY- CLICK- CLICK-

MOTHER, I CAN CLICK OUT THE WHOLE ALPHABET. LISTEN. "A"-"B"-"C".

MY LITTLE GIRL! GOING TO BE A **WAC**.

DICK TRACY

WHY DOES THAT PERSON PLAYING THE PIANO UPSTAIRS HAVE TO **STOMP SO HARD**? WHAT'S THAT?

TAP TAP

FLATTOP SAID THE GIRL DOWNSTAIRS WAS STUDYING TELEGRAPHY. GOOD!

IF SHE'S LEARNING MORSE CODE, THIS STOMPING **MAY** ATTRACT HER ATTENTION.

YES. I'D **SWEAR IT!** HE STOMPED OUT A "D" AND AN "I"— AND —"C"... HUH?

DICK TRACY

"DICK TRACY. — CALLING— POLICE. CONTACT— HEADQUARTERS - HASTE."

I'VE GOT IT.

LISTEN. HAVE YOU **GOT** TO BEAT THE FLOOR LIKE THAT? DO YOU WANT TO SCARE THE PEOPLE DOWNSTAIRS, HUH?

TOO NOISY, EH?

WHERE ARE YOU **GOING**, MARGIE?

I'M TAKING A CAB TO **POLICE HEADQUARTERS**. THAT'S WHERE I'M GOING.

DICK TRACY

ER- PARDON ME. MY NAME'S MARGIE ELONG. I- ER- ARE YOU LOOKING FOR MR. TRACY?

ARE WE LOOKING FOR HIM!

GIRL, THE **DEPARTMENT'S FRANTIC!** WHAT DO YOU **KNOW ABOUT** HIM?

YES, WE'VE DECIDED TO PAY. WE'LL PLACE THE FIFTY THOUSAND DOLLARS ACCORDING TO YOUR PLANS.

THANK YOU, GENTLEMEN.

AH, HA, HA, HA, HA. IT WON'T BE LONG NOW!

FLATTOP

DICK TRACY

NOT BAD, PATTON! YOU'RE VERY PRETTY. VERY PRETTY.

G'WAN WITH YOU, CHIEF.

NOW, MURPHY, I WANT YOU AND NOLAN TO GO ALONG WITH ME AND WAIT ON THE SIDEWALK. THEN—

LATER

OH, MOTHER, IT'S SO EXCITING. WE'RE GOING TO HAVE A REAL POLICE RAID. THEY'RE COMING RIGHT HERE.

RIGHT HERE?? WHY NOT UPSTAIRS?

I JUST CAME FROM THE BIG SHOT'S PLACE, FLATTOP. THE MONEY HAS BEEN PUT UP.

GOOD. THEN WE CAN PROCEED.

DICK TRACY

HM-M-M ♪ ♩ ♪ ♪ ♪

COME IN, MR. PATTON.

MR. PATTON?

YES, IN CASE THE GENTLEMEN UPSTAIRS WERE RUBBER-NECKING OUT OF THEIR WINDOWS, I DIDN'T WANT THEM TO RECOGNIZE ME.

WELL, I DECLARE IT IS A MAN.

THIS WOULD BE A LOT QUIETER, FLATTOP, AND JUST AS QUICK.

NO. WAIT.

DICK TRACY

YOU SAY THE MONEY'S BEEN PAID AND I'M DOOMED TO DIE, EH? WELL, LET'S GO.

DON'T WORRY, YOU'RE GOING, DETECTIVE.

HAVE YOU GOT THE SILENCER FIXED FOR THE AUTOMATIC?

YEAH, FLATTOP, ALL SET.

OKAY. TO YOUR STATIONS, BOYS.

WALK OVER HERE, DETECTIVE. YOU AND I ARE GOING TO HAVE OUR LAST WORDS.

DICK TRACY

TURNING THAT BULB IN THE LAMP IS MAKING THEIR RADIO CLICK. I CAN HEAR IT.

S-I-T T-I-G-H-T H-E-L-P C-O-M-I-N-G

JUST TO LET HIM KNOW WE GOT HIS MESSAGE.

CLICK CLICK

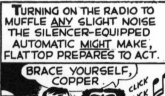

TURNING ON THE RADIO TO MUFFLE ANY SLIGHT NOISE THE SILENCER-EQUIPPED AUTOMATIC MIGHT MAKE, FLATTOP PREPARES TO ACT.

BRACE YOURSELF, COPPER

CLICK CLICK CLICK

ONE- TWO—

-THREE! YOU DIRTY DOGS! ＊!!★!~

TAT-RAT-TAT

158

DICK TRACY

TAKING A DESPERATE CHANCE, DICK TRACY **GRABS FLATTOP'S** HAND.

SILENCER EQUIPPED

SPLAT

THE DEFLECTED BULLET PASSES THROUGH THE MACHINE GUNNER BEHIND TRACY, AS THE THREE MEN FALL TO THE FLOOR.

HOLD YOUR FIRE, MEN! YOU MAY HIT **ME**

HEY!

DROP THAT GUN, FLATTOP!

DICK TRACY

TRACY DIVES FOR THE MACHINE GUN NEAR THE FALLEN GANGSTER.

COME ON, YOU MUGS. START EATING A LITTLE OF THIS.

RA-TAT-TA

DICK TRACY

WHY, YOU DIRTY COPPER -UH-

THIS IS NO PLACE FOR **ME!** I'LL GO DOWN THIS WAY.

FIRE ESCAPE

MURPHY'S AT THE FIRE ESCAPE AND THERE'RE TWO MEN IN FRONT.

COME ON WE'RE GOING UP!

RAT-TAT-TAT

I ALWAYS CARRY A SPARE IN MY OVERCOAT!

DICK TRACY

HE NICKED ME IN THE SIDE, **BUT–**

SUBWAY

TRACY! YE GODS! -A SECOND FRONT.

I THINK THAT CLEANS THEM UP.

MEANWHILE, HAVING MADE HIS WAY DOWN INTO THE NEAREST SUBWAY, FLATTOP PONDERS HIS NEXT MOVE

YOWEE! WHAT A SCREWY LOOKING PAN ON THIS MUG. THINK I'LL PICK HIS POCKET.

159

FLATTOP

DICK TRACY

DICK TRACY

DICK TRACY

DICK TRACY

DICK TRACY

WELL, YOU'RE DEAD! I JUST PHONED THE STORY TO THE PAPERS! BUT I DON'T SEE WHY YOU WANT TO WAIT HERE IN FLATTOP'S APARTMENT.

NOW, PAT, WE'RE GOING TO SIT AND WAIT FOR FLATTOP'S TELEPHONE TO RING.

I DON'T GET IT, TRACY.

THOSE BIG SHOTS WHO HIRED FLATTOP ARE GOING TO TELEPHONE HERE TO CONGRATULATE HIM WHEN THEY SEE THOSE HEADLINES AND— NOW, DO YOU GET IT?

IS IT MUCH FARTHER TO YOUR HOUSE, BUD?

NOT MUCH. WE'LL CUT THROUGH THIS CULVERT TO SAVE TIME.

DICK TRACY

THE SKIPPER WANTS A FULL PAGE OF TRACY PHOTOS AND MORE DETAILS ON FLATTOP.

TELL THE MORGUE TO SEND UP ALL THEIR FILES.

The Daily SEEK BODY OF DETECTIVE DICK TRACY

HERE YOU ARE, TRACY, THE EARLY EDITIONS HAVE YOU SPREAD ALL OVER!

HEY, MISTER, HERE'S YOUR CHANGE.

KEEP IT. KEEP IT. AH, HA, HA, HA! OH BOY!

SO YOUR DAD'S DEAD AND YOUR MOTHER WORKS IN A WAR PLANT?

YEAH, SHE'S ON THE NIGHT SHIFT. HOW DO YOU LIKE THIS LAYOUT, EH?

"SEEK BODY OF DETECTIVE DICK TRACY." WOW!

GENTLEMEN! GENTLEMEN!

IF THE BIG SHOTS DO CALL, REMEMBER OUR ARRANGEMENTS, PAT.

I GOT IT, TRACY. I'M ALL SET.

ALL I NEED IS A ROOM. REMEMBER—NO MEALS.

HERE COMES MA. SHE'S STOPPING ON THE STEPS TO PICK UP THE PAPER. NOW, LEAVE EVERYTHING TO ME.

DICK TRACY

YES, YOU MAY HAVE THE ROOM, AND I'LL EXPECT THE RENT EVERY MONDAY IN ADVANCE.

AND, BUD, BE SURE AND TELL THAT NEWSBOY TO BE MORE CAREFUL WITH OUR PAPER. JUST LOOK AT THE PIECE TORN OUT OF THIS ONE.

YES'M

GET OUT THE BOTTLES, BOYS. FLATTOP'S COMING OVER TO CELEBRATE WITH US. BOY, AM I GLAD I CALLED HIM UP!

MAYBE WE CAN GET BACK SOME OF OUR FIFTY GRAND

I KNEW THEY'D CALL WHEN THEY SAW THOSE HEADLINES! LET'S GO, BOYS.

HOT DOG! 320 MASON STREET, ROOM 400.

FLATTOP

162

DICK TRACY

DICK TRACY

DICK TRACY

DICK TRACY

DICK TRACY

FLATTOP

DICK TRACY

DICK TRACY

DICK TRACY

DICK TRACY

164

FLATTOP

FLATTOP

DICK TRACY

THERE— THAT DIDN'T TAKE LONG. NOW— JUST ANOTHER FOR GOOD MEASURE!

WHEN TWO SMART GUYS MEET, ONE ALWAYS HAS TO LOSE!

NOW, FOR THE LAST BOTTLE OF THIS GASOLINE "DRY CLEANER."

THEN— A MATCH— AND— AHA, HA, HA— YES, WHEN TWO SMART GUYS MEET, ONE ALWAYS LOSES!

DICK TRACY

LITTLE BOTTLES OF "MAGIC CLEANER," EH— MARVEL OF THE AGE FOR REMOVING SPOTS, EH? WELL, REMOVE THIS SPOT.

THE GASOLINE-DRENCHED CLOTHING BURSTS INTO VIOLENT FLAME.

A PAIR OF FEET MOVE SWIFTLY FROM THE DREARY HALLWAY AND DOWN THE STREET.

AND WHERE TWO MEN STOOD BEFORE, ONE PRONE FORM LIES UNCONSCIOUS, WRAPPED IN SEETHING FLAME

WELL, THIS IS A SURPRISING TURN OF EVENTS. H'M?

DICK TRACY

GET AROUND ON THE OTHER SIDE, ANDREWS. THAT'S IT!

PROP THE HALL DOOR OPEN. GET SOME AIR IN HERE

WHO IS HE?

YEAH —A BILLFOLD. IT WAS LAYING OVER AGAINST THE WALL

WHAT'S THE NAME INSIDE?

WHAT? BURNED TO DEATH IN A HALLWAY? HOLD EVERYTHING. WE'LL BE RIGHT DOWN.

DICK TRACY

THIS MAN IS HAWKER DAVIS, A PITCHMAN WHO'S WORKED THE AVENUE FOR YEARS.

FLATTOP MUST HAVE MADE HAWKER EXCHANGE CLOTHES WITH HIM.

FLATTOP'S IDEA WAS TO MAKE THE POLICE THINK HE (FLATTOP) HAD BEEN BURNED TO DEATH.

RIGHT, PAT.

AND AT THE CORNER NEWSSTAND AT THE LOWER END OF THE CITY.

IT'S A WAR BOND! IT JUST BLEW DOWN ONTO MY NEWSSTAND. MUST HAVE BLOWN OUT OF A CAR.

WHO WOULD HAVE THOUGHT THAT STREET HAWKER HAD WAR BONDS IN HIS COAT POCKET! OOPS! WH— DID ONE FLY OUT THE WINDOW?

DICK TRACY

IT MUST HAVE BLOWN OUT OF THE WINDOW—FROM THE TOP OF THE DRESSER.

HEY! LOOK AT THE NAME ON THIS WAR BOND. WELL, I'LL BE— I'VE HEARD OF HIM!

YEAH. THAT NEWSBOY AND HIS FRIEND ARE HOLDING A PIECE OF PAPER. THEY'RE LOOKING UP HERE!

THE NAME SAYS "HAWKER DAVIS." MAYBE HE LIVES IN THAT CHEAP HOTEL!

BUT I TELL YOU, HE CAN'T BE LIVING IN THAT HOTEL. LOOK! HE'S THE MUG WHO'S JUST BEEN MURDERED!

DICK TRACY

LOOK, THIS WAR BOND JUST BLEW DOWN ONTO MY NEWSSTAND. IT'S MADE OUT TO HAWKER DAVIS, THE MAN WHO WAS JUST MURDERED.

WHAT'S THIS?

IT MUST HAVE BLOWN OUT OF THAT HOTEL. LOOK, THERE'S ONLY ONE WINDOW OPEN.

KEEP YOUR EYE ON THAT WINDOW, SON, WHILE I USE A CALL BOX.

THE KID TALKED TO THE COP — THE COP'S USING A CALL BOX — I'VE GOT TO MOVE.

BY THE TIME I'D GET DOWN TO THE MAIN FLOOR, COPS WOULD BE SWARMING ALL OVER. I'VE GOT TO HIDE INSIDE THIS HOTEL.

DICK TRACY

I HEAR A POLICE SIREN ALREADY! I'D BETTER LOOK FOR A VACANT ROOM AND SLIP INSIDE.

NO DOORS ARE AJAR. I'LL HAVE TO TRY THE KNOBS AND JUST SAY I MADE A MISTAKE, IF THE ROOM'S OCCUPIED.

YES, VITAMIN FLINTHEART, YOU STILL HAVE THAT SNAP AND DASH IN SPITE OF YOUR FIFTY YEARS.

WHY SHOULDN'T YOU STAGE A HOLLYWOOD COMEBACK — UH — HUH ???

DICK TRACY

HUH ??

ALL RIGHT, MY GOOD FELLOW, WHAT'S THIS ALL ABOUT?

OH-UH-I'M SORRY. I WAS LOOKING FOR THE ROOM OF A FRIEND.

DO YOU CUSTOMARILY ENTER A FRIEND'S ROOM BACKWARDS, SIR?

YEAH, IT'S A WAR BOND BELONGING TO THE MURDERED STREET HAWKER.

EH? LET'S SEE.

FLATTOP

DICK TRACY

TO TELL THE TRUTH, MISTER, I'M NOT WELL. I FELT A FAINTING SPELL COMING ON. AND I STEPPED INTO THE FIRST ROOM I SAW

IN THAT CASE, OLD FELLOW, SIT DOWN! VITAMIN FLINTHEART WELCOMES YOU TO HIS HUMBLE ABODE.

YOU'RE SURE I'M NOT INTRUDING?

COME, COME, OLD BOY, WE ACTORS WON'T BITE, YOU KNOW.

VITAMIN PILLS

MAKEUP KIT

DICK TRACY

WE CAME UP TO THIS FLOOR **TO LOOK FOR A GUNMAN!** WE HEARD YOU **GROAN.**

OH-H-H-H! HE HIT ME—HE HIT ME.

YE GODS. LOOK AT THE FACE CREAM—AND POWDER PUFFS AND **WIGS!**

WHO ARE YOU, OLD MAN?

OLD MAN? **FAW!** I AM **VITAMIN FLINTHEART,** THE GREAT ACTOR! IDOL OF MILLIONS.

MEANWHILE IN THE HOTEL LOBBY.

HE DIDN'T WANT TO PART WITH THE WIG. BUT AFTER ALL I'M MERELY BORROWING IT.

DICK TRACY

WELL, FLATTOP, YOU'RE DOING ALL RIGHT, SO FAR. IF ONLY THIS MUSTACHE AND FACE PUTTY HOLD OUT.

HOTEL

TAXI!

WHERE'LL IT BE, POP?

ZOUNDS, GENTLEMEN, THE BOUNDER TOOK ADVANTAGE OF MY KINDLY DISPOSITION! THAT FIENDISH FACE. THAT FLAT HEAD! I CAN SEE THEM. **NOW!**

FLAT HEAD?

AND LITTLE ROUND MOUTH?

AH, YES! IN ALL MY DAYS, VITAMIN FLINTHEART NEVER LAID EYES ON SUCH AN UGLY PUSS.

DICK TRACY

—THAT'S THE STORY, GENTLEMEN. HE **ENTERED.** HE **BOPPED ME**—HE **DEPARTED!**

YOUR DESCRIPTION FITS **FLATTOP** EXACTLY! HE SPIED YOUR MAKE-UP KIT AND THAT GAVE HIM IDEAS.

JUST WHAT WOULD YOU SAY HE WORE, VITAMIN, WHEN HE LEFT YOU?

AFTER INVOICING, I WOULD SAY THE CAD TOOK ONE CIGARET HOLDER, ONE WIG, ONE MUSTACHE, (SLIGHTLY USED) AND—AH YES, MY CHERISHED **CANE!**

IS IT MUCH FURTHER?

JUST AROUND THE CORNER, POP. WE'LL BE THERE IN A SECOND

170

DICK TRACY

AH, THIS EXCITEMENT HAS UNSTRUNG ME! MY **NERVES!** UGH. HAND ME MY BISMUTH AND MY VITAMIN PILLS, LAD.

STAY WITH **HIM**, PAT! I'LL TAKE THE OFFICERS AND WE'LL COMB THE BUILDING.

YEAH, COME TO THINK OF IT, I DID SEE AN OLD FELLOW, GRAY HAIR, LONG CIGARET HOLDER, DERBY. HE WENT THROUGH THE LOBBY AND TOOK A CAB.

IN THE DARKNESS OF THE MOVIE, I CAN SIT UNDISTURBED. I'VE GOT TO HAVE TIME TO THINK.

ONE, PLEASE.

DICK TRACY

YEAH, THIS IS A CHEAP HOTEL. MINE IS THE ONLY HACK THAT WORKS OUT OF HERE.

THEN YOU COULD TELL ME IF A GRAY-HAIRED GUY WITH A DERBY AND LONG CIGARET HOLDER HOPPED YOUR CAB A FEW MINUTES AGO.

I **SURE CAN** AND I CAN TELL YOU **RIGHT WHERE** I **TOOK** HIM, TOO!

NOW, MY **NERVE TONIC**, MY BOY! EGAD! I'M FALLING APART!

AH— I FEEL SAFER I PICKED OUT THIS SEAT RIGHT IN FRONT OF A POST SO I WON'T HAVE TO TAKE OFF MY HAT. HA!

DICK TRACY

THAT'S THE PLACE, MR. TRACY. **VISTA THEATRE.**

OKAY, DRIVER! TURN AROUND!

KEEP ALL THIS TO YOURSELF FOR A COUPLE OF HOURS. THERE'S GOING TO BE FIREWORKS APLENTY.

YOU BET I WILL. AND THANKS.

AS THE GREAT BARD ONCE SAID — **UH** —

OH — UGH — UFF — NO — NO — QUICK — MY BISMUTH! MY **BISMUTH!**

BURP

DICK TRACY

THAT'S **HIM!**

WHAT? THAT **ISN'T** FLATTOP.

LOOK OUT, TRACY!

FLATTOP **ISN'T** WEARING THE WIG!

WE'VE GOT YOU **COVERED**, FLATTOP.

SAY, **THAT** GUY GAVE ME THIS **WIG AND DERBY** — IN THE THEATRE.

I POINTED TO THIS LAD AND SAID, "THAT'S HIM." IF THE DETECTIVE HAD PULLED THE TRIGGER, I WOULD HAVE BEEN THE CAUSE OF AN **INNOCENT BOY'S DEATH.**

TAKE IT EASY, VITAMIN.

HUH?

DICK TRACY

EASY, **FLATTOP**, YOU'RE **BADLY WOUNDED**.

I'LL PIN HIS FEET.

I WAS JUST SITTING THERE IN THE MOVIE WHEN HE SAID HE'D BEEN TO A BIG MASQUERADE— AND ASKED ME IF I WANTED HIS WIG AND DERBY.

TO THINK I POINTED AT YOU! MR. TRACY MIGHT HAVE SHOT YOU!

I WOULD HAVE HAD THE BLOOD OF AN **INNOCENT BOY** ON MY HANDS.

HERE, VITAMIN, QUIT BLUBBERING AND HOLD FLATTOP'S **GUN**.

Reg. U. S. Pat. Off.: Copyright, 1944, by The Chicago Tribune.

I WOULD HAVE GONE THROUGH LIFE KNOWING I HAD CAUSED THIS INNOCENT LAD'S **DEATH**. OH-H-H-H.

CHESTER GOULD

DICK TRACY

BLOOD MAKES ME ILL. I FEEL **FAINT**. ALAS! VIOLENCE NAUSEATES ME!

I SHALL WITHDRAW FROM THIS GRIZZLY SCENE. VITAMIN FLINTHEART'S FORTE IS NOT IN CRIMINOLOGY.

I SHALL SEEK OUT SOME QUIET NOOK TO REASSEMBLE MY SHATTERED NERVES. SOME PLACE TO COMPOSE MYSELF AND THINK.

X-RAY VIEW SHOWS FLATTOP'S GUN, WHICH PAT PATTON ASKED VITAMIN TO HOLD

OKAY, **TAKE 'ER AWAY**. CENTRAL HOSPITAL, DRIVER!

H'M. WHERE'S VITAMIN FLINTHEART?

Reg. U. S. Pat. Off. Copyright, 1944, by The Chicago Tribune.

CHESTER GOULD

DICK TRACY

I'LL KILL EVERY COPPER IN TOWN FOR THIS—I'LL—

LIE DOWN, FLATTOP.

3-25-44 Reg. U. S. Pat. Off.: Copyright, 1944, by The Chicago Tribune.

GET THE **STRAPS**.

HE'S **VIOLENT**.

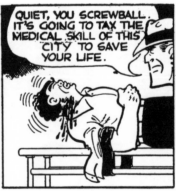

QUIET, YOU SCREWBALL. IT'S GOING TO TAX THE MEDICAL SKILL OF THIS CITY TO SAVE YOUR LIFE.

TO THINK THAT I MIGHT HAVE CAUSED THE DEATH OF THAT INNOCENT LAD. EGAD! I'M ALL **UNSTRUNG**.

JOE'S

CHESTER GOULD

UNSTRUNG! NERVES COMPLETELY UNSTRUNG! PERCHANCE, A WEE SIP OF SOME TONIC MIGHT PULL ME TOGETHER

CRIMINOLOGY WAS NEVER INTENDED FOR VITAMIN FLINTHEART! BLOOD, BODIES, SHOOTING! UGH! GRUESOME! GHASTLY!

YES, FLATTOP, YOU'LL LIVE.

GOOD.

Reg. U. S. Pat. Off.: Copyright, 1944, by The Chicago Tribune.

—AND THAT INNOCENT LAD WHOSE DEATH I NEARLY CAUSED UGH—**WAITER**!

THE FORGOTTEN GUN OF FLATTOP'S, STILL REPOSING IN THE ACTOR'S POCKET

CHESTER GOULD

THE SUMMER SISTERS, THE BROW, AND GRAVEL GERTIE

1944

SUMMER SISTERS, THE BROW, GRAVEL GERTIE

DICK TRACY

DICK TRACY

DICK TRACY

DICK TRACY

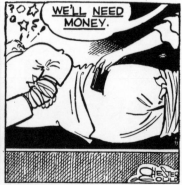

DICK TRACY

DICK TRACY

DICK TRACY

DICK TRACY

SUMMER SISTERS, THE BROW, GRAVEL GERTIE

DICK TRACY

YOU SAY THOSE FIELD GLASSES ARE IN THE HANDS OF TWO GIRLS.

YES, BROW.

I WANT THOSE GLASSES AND WANT THEM NOW.

BUT, BROW, THE PLACE IS UNDER SURVEILLANCE BY NAVY MEN.

DID I ASK YOU FOR A LITERARY DESCRIPTION OF THE PLACE? I WANT THOSE GLASSES!

NO, BROW. NOT THAT! I'LL GET THE GLASSES!

YOUR FINGERPRINT RECORD SHOWS YOUR NAME IS NOFFEL YOU WERE CONVICTED OF ESPIONAGE DURING THE LAST WAR AND YOU ENTERED THIS COUNTRY ILLEGALLY IN 1938! NOW, DO YOU CARE TO CARRY ON FROM THERE?

DICK TRACY

MAY, WHERE ARE YOU GOING?

I'VE GOT TO GET RID OF THIS GUN WE TOOK FROM MR. PATTON.

WE DON'T WANT THE POLICE TO FIND IT ON US! YOU STAY THERE, I'LL BE RIGHT BACK.

AH! THE BATHROOM LINEN CLOSET! I'LL PUT IT UNDER THESE WINTER BEDCLOTHES.

PAT. GO TO THAT ROOMING HOUSE AND GET THE LANDLADY TO GIVE YOU A LIST OF NAMES OF ALL HER ROOMERS. ALSO KEYS TO EVERY ROOM IN HER HOUSE

DICK TRACY

SHIP 29 ON CHART DEPARTED N.E TOWARD NEWFOUNDLAND 12 A.M. CONVOY FORMING OFF CAPE NESS THAT IS ALL—BROW.

HAS 12 RECOVERED THOSE FIELD GLASSES FROM THE TWO SISTERS

I DON'T KNOW, BROW. HE'S SUPPOSED TO REPORT BACK HERE IN ONE HOUR.

VITAMIN! WHAT ARE YOU DOING HERE?

AH! WHAT AM I DOING?" HE SAYS! WHY, I'VE BEEN WAITING DAYS TO SEE MR. TRACY.

I KNOW WHERE THE SUMMER SISTERS ARE LIVING. BUT IS ANYONE INTERESTED? THEY ARE NOT. EGAD! I'M IGNORED!

DICK TRACY

FINALLY CONTACTING DICK TRACY, VITAMIN FLINTHEART POINTS OUT THE ROOM THE SUMMER SISTERS SO RECENTLY OCCUPIED.

I CAN'T GET OVER IT! THAT'S THE SAME BUILDING WHERE WE PICKED UP THE SPY.

MR. TRACY, I HAVE SOME VERY INTERESTING NEWS REGARDING THE SUMMER SISTERS.

LIEUTENANT CLARK! I DIDN'T KNOW YOU WERE ON DUTY HERE. WHAT IS YOUR NEWS?

SO THEY WERE GOING TO PAWN OUR FIELD GLASSES, EH?? LET ME CONGRATULATE YOU, 12, ON BRINGING THE YOUNG LADIES HERE TO ME.

THE BROW LIKES YOUNG LADIES. PARTICULARLY NICE YOUNG LADIES WHO MIGHT BE SEEKING JOBS AT BIG PAY.

DID YOU SAY JOBS, SIR?

180

DICK TRACY

YOU SEE, AS ANOTHER NAVY INTELLIGENCE MAN ASSIGNED TO THIS JOB, I'D BEGUN TO THINK THINGS WERE PRETTY DULL, WHEN OUT OF THAT ROOMING HOUSE, CAME THE SUMMER SISTERS.

THEY LEFT THEIR ROOMING HOUSE WITH A PACKAGE. SUDDENLY THEY WERE PICKED UP BY A MAN WHO SHOVED THEM INTO A CAR AND BROUGHT THEM TO THIS OLD POPCORN STAND.

YOU MEAN THE SUMMER SISTERS AND THEIR CAPTORS CAME INTO **THIS** LITTLE PEANUT SHACK

RIGHT. SAY ISN'T THAT A TRAP DOOR IN THE FLOOR?

NOW, **IF I DO** GIVE YOU JOBS I WANT TO FEEL I CAN **TRUST** YOU. THE WORK YOU WILL DO CALLS FOR HONESTY.

HONESTY? OH, SIR, HONESTY IS OUR MIDDLE NAME— ESPECIALLY IF IT'S FOR MONEY.

DICK TRACY

YES, SIR, TRACY, I TRAILED THE SUMMER SISTERS TO THIS ABANDONED PEANUT STAND, AND APPARENTLY THAT TRAP DOOR LEADS TO A HIDEOUT.

THE TRAP DOOR IS LOCKED, BUT JUST LISTEN TO THAT DOWN DRAFT. THERE'S A TERRIFIC AIR SUCTION THROUGH HERE.

I WONDER WHERE THAT DOOR LEADS? IF WE COULD FIND THE BACK ENTRANCE TO THEIR PLACE WE'D HAVE A BETTER CHANCE.

THAT DOWN DRAFT GIVES ME AN IDEA. WE'LL **FIND** THE BACK ENTRANCE!

GO TO THE NEAREST DRUG STORE AND GET ME ABOUT **FIVE OUNCES OF THE STRONGEST PERFUME YOU CAN FIND.**

WHAT?

DICK TRACY

YES, SIR, THIS TRAP DOOR LEADS TO THEIR HIDEOUT SOMEWHERE BACK IN THOSE OLD BUILDINGS.

HERE'S THE PERFUME YOU SENT ME FOR, TRACY.

GOOD, LIEUTENANT.

THE TERRIFIC DOWN DRAFT AROUND THIS TRAP DOOR MEANS THERE'S A STRONG AIR FLOW THROUGH THEIR QUARTERS. WE'LL JUST **POUR THIS PERFUME AROUND THE DOOR**

NOW YOU AND I ARE GOING TO SNIFF ALL VENTILATORS AND REAR DOORS BACK IN THIS ALLEY TILL WE FIND WHERE THE PERFUME COMES OUT.

DICK TRACY

NOW, LET'S TALK TURKEY, SUMMER SISTERS. YOU KIDS AREN'T HANGING AROUND THIS TOWN FOR YOUR HEALTH! YOU WANT TO MAKE **BIG DOUGH**, EH?

PERFUME TRACY POURED AROUND TRAP DOOR

WELL, YOU SEE, WE CAME TO THIS TOWN TO GO INTO RADIO. THERE'S BIG MONEY THERE.

RADIO, **BAH!** I MEAN TWENTY-FIVE OR FIFTY OR MAYBE A **HUNDRED DOLLARS A DAY.**

SAY! WHERE'S THAT PERFUME ODOR COMING FROM?

DON'T KNOW BROW. IT MUST BE ON THE SUMMER SISTERS.

HERE YOU ARE, TRACY! THE PERFUME'S COMING OUT RIGHT HERE.

DICK TRACY

YOU'RE RIGHT, LIEUTENANT. THE PERFUME'S COMING FROM THIS VENTILATOR.

3 FLOORS DOWN

IT GOES INTO THE BUILDING AT THIS POINT. THAT WOULD BE THE CEILING OF THE BASEMENT.

FIRST, WE'LL UNCOUPLE THIS JOINT. WATCH IT. THIS USED TO BE AN OLD RESTAURANT. THERE'S PROBABLY GREASE ON THE PIPES.

SH-SH- EASY, LIEUTENANT. I HEAR VOICES. — WOMEN'S VOICES.

OH THANK YOU, SIR! YOU'RE WONDERFUL.

DICK TRACY

YES, YOU CAN SQUARE YOUR-SELVES WITH ME IF YOU'LL JUST SIT TIGHT AND DO AS I SAY! PLAY BALL WITH THIS BROW PERSON TILL WE'RE READY TO SPRING

WE'LL DO JUST AS YOU SAY, MR. TRACY! WE'RE SORRY WE WERE EVER BAD AND WE WANT TO SQUARE OURSELVES.

GOOD! JUST BE PATIENT.

THESE PEOPLE ARE NOTHING BUT SPIES, MAY, AND WE'VE GOT TO HELP MR. TRACY CATCH THEM.

SH-SH! LISTEN.

GOOD MORNING, TURTLE! EVERYTHING OKAY?

OH-ER- UH— HELLO, BROW.

SURE, SURE!

DICK TRACY

BRING OUR LITTLE LADIES IN, TURTLE! THEY MUST FEEL QUITE REFRESHED AFTER THEIR NIGHT'S REST.

PLEASE DON'T BREAK OUR OTHER WRISTS, MR. BROW! WE'LL DO ANYTHING YOU SAY.

I JUST WANTED YOU TO KNOW WHO'S BOSS!

YOU'RE TO STAY HERE WHERE YOU CAN WATCH THAT OLD PEANUT SHACK, PAT. THAT'S THE ENTRANCE TO THEIR DEN. IF THE SUMMER SISTERS COME OUT, TAIL THEM CONSTANTLY.

TODAY, YOU START EARNING 25 DOLLARS A DAY, MERELY BY RUNNING ERRANDS. BRING IN THE SPIKE MACHINE, TURTLE.

DICK TRACY

ANYTHING NEW, LIEUTENANT?

NO. I'VE BEEN HEARING VOICES BUT I CAN'T MAKE OUT WHAT THEY'RE SAYING.

THAT'S IT, TURTLE, PUSH IT OVER IN THE CORNER.

WHAT IS THAT? OH —PLEASE— PLEASE—

EASY, LADIES, EASY.

NOTHING'S GOING TO HURT YOU. I'M JUST GOING TO TELL YOU WHAT YOUR DUTIES WILL BE. YOU WANT TO EARN 25 DOLLARS A DAY, DON'T YOU?

DICK TRACY

GOOD NIGHT, GIRLS YOU'LL FIND HOT FOOD ON THE TABLE

OH, JUNE, DID THAT SPIKE MACHINE HURT YOU BADLY? I-I RAN THE ERRAND AS FAST AS I COULD.

MAY, WE'VE GOT TO GET OUT OF HERE THEY—THEY'RE BAD MEN. THEY MIGHT EVEN MURDER US.

MAY! WHAT ARE YOU THINKING OF??

I JUST HAPPENED TO REMEMBER THE PISTOL WE TOOK FROM MR. PATTON AND HID IN THAT ROOMING HOUSE LINEN CLOSET!

I WONDER IF IT'S STILL THERE?

DICK TRACY

IT'S OUR ONLY HOPE, JUNE—THAT GUN IN THE ROOMING HOUSE CLOSET

SH-SH! THE BROW'S CALLING US

GOOD MORNING, LADIES. ARE YOU ALL READY FOR ANOTHER BUSY DAY?

SIT DOWN, MAY, DARLING, IN THE COZY LITTLE CHAIR. AND YOU, TURTLE, GIVE JUNE INSTRUCTIONS ON THE ERRAND SHE'S TO RUN.

PAT, CALL NESTOR AND GOODROW AND ZOY FROM THE EXERCISE ROOM. WE'RE GOING TO VISIT THAT HANGOUT THE SUMMER SISTERS ARE OCCUPYING — NOW!

DICK TRACY

YOU HAVE 23 MINUTES, JUNE, TO GO TO THIS ADDRESS A MAN IN A JANITOR'S UNIFORM WILL GIVE YOU A SEALED ENVELOPE

IF YOU FAIL TO RETURN IN THE GIVEN TIME YOU KNOW THE FATE THAT AWAITS YOUR SISTER

THE CLOCK'S ALL SET, BROW.

THAT ROOMING HOUSE! —THAT PISTOL HID IN THE LINEN CLOSET! I'VE GOT TO GET IT IN 23 MINUTES!

HOT POPCORN

POPCORN

YOU GIRLS HAVEN'T HAD YOUR BREAKFAST YET, BUT YOU SHALL HAVE IT AS SOON AS YOUR SISTER RETURNS — THAT IS, IF YOU HAVE AN APPETITE.

TICK TOCK

YOUR SISTER IS 2 MINUTES LATE. ARE THE SPIKES STARTING TO HURT?

SHE'S HERE, BROW!

WELL—LET'S HAVE THE ENVELOPE, MY DEAR YOUR SISTER'S SUFFERING!

I DIDN'T GET AN ENVELOPE. BUT I DID GET A .38 THAT MY SISTER AND I HAD HID IN A ROOMING HOUSE LINEN CLOSET

OH, NO YOU DON'T! WE CAME FROM THE MOUNTAINS WHERE A GIRL LEARNS TO SHOOT! TURN OFF THAT MACHINE, BROW!

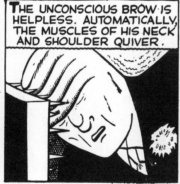

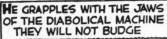

DICK TRACY

PULLING THE ELECTRIC CORD TO THE SPIKE MACHINE STOPS IT FROM FURTHER CLOSING— BUT IT **DOES NOT** FREE THE BROW

HE GRAPPLES WITH THE JAWS OF THE DIABOLICAL MACHINE. THEY WILL NOT BUDGE

CRUNCH CRACK

TICK TOCK TOCK

EVERY MOMENT BRINGS EXCRUCIATING PAIN.

IF I TRY TO PULL MYSELF FREE I'LL **TEAR** THE FLESH RIGHT **OFF.**

SO! THERE SHE IS! COME HERE, SISTER, WE WANT YOU, TOO.

BUT I TELL YOU, WE WEREN'T TRYING TO MAKE A GETAWAY. WE WERE **WAITING** FOR **YOU!**

DICK TRACY

I'VE **GOT** TO DO IT. I'LL GRIT MY TEETH AND YANK!

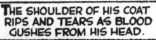

THE SHOULDER OF HIS COAT RIPS AND TEARS AS BLOOD GUSHES FROM HIS HEAD.

THE BROW STRUGGLES TO HIS FEET AND LEANS HEAVILY ON THE WATER COOLER AS THE SOUND OF FOOTSTEPS REACHES HIS EARS.

I TELL YOU HE'S IN HERE!— AND TWO OF HIS MEN— DEAD! RIGHT DOWN THIS CORRIDOR.

DICK TRACY

YE GODS! SHE WAS TELLING THE TRUTH!

BUT THE **BROW!** HE—HE'S **GONE!**

LOOK OUT!— THERE ARE FRESH BLOOD SPOTS! THEY STOP AT THE **WATER COOLER.**

THERE ARE ONLY 2 ROOMS AND THAT ROOM HAS NO **EXIT.**

WHERE COULD HE HAVE **GONE?**

DICK TRACY

CAN YOU IMAGINE THAT! THIS WATER COOLER MOVES, REVEALING AN **EXIT** TO THE REAR.

WELL, BOYS, WE FOUND OUT HOW THE BROW GOT OUT. BUT WHERE DID HE GO?

WELL, BILL, THIS IS THE FIRST TIME OUR LABORATORY HAS BEEN ASKED TO TEST A PLASTIC CASKET, EH?

YEAH— WE'RE SUPPOSED TO SUBMERGE IT IN WATER FOR 10 DAYS. PUT THE CHAINS AROUND IT WHILE I GET THE RECORD BOOK TO MAKE OUT THE TIME SHEET.

DICK TRACY

MY PARTNER HAD A HEART ATTACK BEFORE — BUT THIS LOOKS LIKE A BAD ONE.

LAY HIM THERE ON THE BENCH.

WERE AFTER A DESPERATE CRIMINAL, MISTER. AS SOON AS YOU CALL THE DOCTOR WE'LL BE ON OUR WAY.

YES, MR. TRACY.

HE'S COMING TO

IN THE CASKET! I-I SAW HIM—HE WAS ALIVE!

DICK TRACY

I DIDN'T HAVE A HEART ATTACK! I SAW A MAN IN THAT CASKET! I FAINTED.

BLOOD SPOTS VERIFY THAT.

BUT I TELL YOU I RUN THE COLD TEST ROOM. MY NAME'S O'BRIEN

NO, MR. TRACY, THAT ISN'T THE BROW

THAT ROOM IS FORTY BELOW ZERO, AND IT'S SOUND PROOF IN THERE. I DIDN'T HEAR ANYONE OR SEE ANYONE.

THAT'S IT, MAY. DRAW US A PICTURE OF THE BROW. YOU GIRLS ARE THE ONLY ONES WHO'VE SEEN HIM SO FAR.

DICK TRACY

YOU GIRLS WILL BE HELD IN POLICE CUSTODY FOR THE TIME BEING. IT'S OBVIOUS THAT THE SHOOTING OF THE BROW'S CONFEDERATES WAS SELF DEFENSE.

WE'VE SEARCHED THIS PLACE FROM FRONT TO BACK, TRACY. THE BROW JUST ISN'T HERE.

TAKE THE SPIKE MACHINE TO HEADQUARTERS AND CONFISCATE HIS SHORT WAVE OUTFIT.

IT'S FIVE O'CLOCK, CHARLIE. SHALL I LOCK UP FOR THE NIGHT?

NO, THE POLICE ARE COMING BACK FOR A FINAL SEARCH.

DICK TRACY

DON'T YOU SEE, GIRLS, YOU'RE OUR KEY WITNESSES? YOU'RE THE ONLY ONES WHO HAVE SEEN THE BROW. WE'VE GOT TO SEE THAT NO HARM BEFALLS YOU

DOES THAT MEAN WE ALL ARE UNDER ARREST?

WELL, IT'S SOMETHING LIKE THAT, LADIES.

I COULDN'T STAY DOWN THERE ANY LONGER— MY HEAD'S BURSTING! MY SKIN'S LIKE ICE

WHAT? NO ONE AROUND? THE PLACE MUST BE LOCKED UP FOR THE NIGHT! HA! THIS IS MY CHANCE!—OR IS IT?

DICK TRACY

Panel 1: DOC! IT'S ME. — THE BROW! LET ME IN. — BROW!

Panel 2: DOC, YOU AND I ARE THE ONLY ONES LEFT! TURTLE AND JOE ARE DEAD, AND 26 IS IN NAVAL CUSTODY.

Panel 3: WE WENT OVER THAT LABORATORY WITH A FINE-TOOTH COMB, TRACY. FINALLY, WE LOCKED THE PLACE UP — AND BEAT IT.

Panel 4: WHAT IS OUR NEXT MOVE, BROW? — OUR NEXT MOVE, DOC, IS TO ERASE TWO WOMEN — TWO LYING, DOUBLE-CROSSING WOMEN.

DICK TRACY

Panel 1: WHAT DID YOU FIND OUT, DOC? — THE SUMMER SISTERS ARE IN POLICE CUSTODY. BUT BENNY THE BONDSMAN SAID THE POLICE ARE GOING TO PLACE 'EM IN A HOTEL ROOM THIS AFTERNOON.

Panel 2: WHAT ARE YOU GETTING DRESSED FOR, BROW? — YOU AND I, DOC, ARE GOING TO GET IN THE CAR AND DO A LITTLE TOURING

Panel 3: I WANT TO SURVEY THE BOULEVARDS AND PICK OUT ALL THE HIGH BRIDGES AND VIADUCTS. — HIGH BRIDGES, EH?

Panel 4: BUT, CHIEF, I DON'T THINK WE OUGHT TO LET THEM OUT OF OUR SIGHT. — MURPHY, CALL THE HOPP HOTEL AND GET A ROOM FOR THESE SUMMER SISTERS. THEY CAN'T STAY HERE.

DICK TRACY

Panel 1: BUT I TELL YOU, CHIEF, THE SUMMER SISTERS' LIVES AREN'T WORTH A NICKEL AS LONG AS THE BROW IS AT LARGE. WHY SEND THEM TO A HOTEL?

Panel 2: WHY NOT KEEP THEM RIGHT HERE IN THE WOMEN'S QUARTERS BEHIND BARS? — BUT WE DON'T WANT TO STAY BEHIND BARS, MR. TRACY. — HM?

Panel 3: BUT, BROW, YOU'VE GOT A LOT OF NERVE PARKING THIS CLOSE TO POLICE HEADQUARTERS. — STAY HERE, I TELL YOU.

Panel 4: AND KEEP YOUR EYES ON THAT POLICE BUILDING ENTRANCE. IF THOSE TWO DAMES COME OUT — THEY'LL NEVER GO BACK!

DICK TRACY

Panel 1: WELL, THAT'S THAT — THAT FINISHES THE SUMMER SISTERS

Panel 2: FORCING THE GIRLS' CAB THROUGH THE BRIDGE RAILING, BROW AND THE DOC SPEED ON — OFFICER MURPHY

Panel 3: IT'S THE SUMMER SISTERS! I WAS ABLE TO JUMP OUT, BUT THEY'RE DOWN THERE!

Panel 4: (GULP) OPEN THE DOOR, MAY. (ULP) — I CAN'T (ULP) I CAN'T — WHAT'LL WE DO?

DICK TRACY

THE **DOOR** WON'T OPEN!

HOLD ON TO ME, MAY-
-OH-MAY! (GLUB)

DOOR WON'T OPEN. (GLUG)

THERE ARE **TWO GIRLS AND A CAB DRIVER DOWN THERE!** I'LL NEVER KNOW HOW I GOT OUT.

THIS LAGOON OPENS INTO THE **RIVER!** CALL A COASTAL PATROL BOAT WE'LL NEED A **DIVER** TO GET INTO THAT CAB.

DICK TRACY

I **SAW** THE CAR THAT FORCED THEM THROUGH THE BRIDGE RAILING. I BELIEVE I COULD IDENTIFY IT.

LET'S GO!

THERE'S LIABLE TO BE A SWARM OF SQUAD CARS AFTER US, DOC! CUT UP TO THE PARK BEACH!

WEARING SWIMMING TRUNKS UNDER HIS CLOTHES, THE BROW DISROBES IN THE CAR, TOSSES A TOWEL OVER HIS HEAD AND PREPARES TO STEP OUT!

BEACH

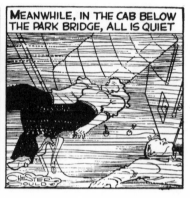

MEANWHILE, IN THE CAB BELOW THE PARK BRIDGE, ALL IS QUIET

DICK TRACY

KEEP GOING, DOC! I'LL MEET YOU AT YOUR PLACE LATE TONIGHT.

BEACH

JUST LIKE ANY OTHER CASUAL SWIMMER, THE BROW SAUNTERS ONTO THE BEACH.

LET THE COPS CHASE DOC'S CAR. I'LL BE SAFE ON THE BEACH.

NONCHALANTLY, HE STRETCHES OUT ON THE SAND, HIS FACE HIDDEN BY THE TOWEL.

THE POOR SUMMER SISTERS! I TOLD THE CHIEF THEY SHOULD NEVER HAVE LEFT HEADQUARTERS.

THIS IS THE SPOT RIGHT HERE.

DICK TRACY

WELL, TESS, YOUR WAC UNIFORM CERTAINLY IS BECOMING.

THANK YOU, JEAN, BUT IT WILL BE NICE TO SHED IT FOR A SWIMMING SUIT.

BEACH HOUSE

IT HARDLY SEEMS POSSIBLE THAT YOU'VE BELONGED SINCE LAST APRIL.

YES, THE TIME REALLY FLIES.

SHALL WE SIT DOWN HERE FOR A SUN BATH?

OKAY.

THE BROW

TRACY, ALL 3 OF THEM ARE DOWN THERE! -DROWNED.

BETTER SEND A CABLE DOWN -WE'LL PULL UP CAB AND ALL.

DICK TRACY

THE POOR SUMMER SISTERS! WHAT A PITY.

YOU CAN PUT AWAY YOUR INHALATOR, BOYS.

BRING THEM OUT ON DECK.

WELL, WAC TRUEHEART, HOW DO YOU LIKE THIS?

HOW PEACEFUL AND RELAXING IT IS TO BE A CIVILIAN! BOY, OH, **BOY!** PEACE AND QUIET!

THE BROW

DICK TRACY

MY **GAS COUPONS!** THEY— I'VE LOST THEM. I HAD THEM RIGHT HERE IN MY BAG.

AND IN THE APARTMENT OF BROW'S CONFEDERATE, DOC.

IT WAS THE BROW. HE SAID HE HAD GAS COUPONS. ENOUGH FOR US TO GET OUT OF TOWN. I WONDER WHERE HE GOT 'EM.

IT'S QUITE WINDY, TESS. THEY MAY HAVE BLOWN OUT OF YOUR BAG.

TWELVE OF 'EM!— THEY BLEW RIGHT INTO MY HANDS. H'M. I'LL WAIT HERE TILL DOC COMES ALONG!

DICK TRACY

TESS, DON'T WORRY SO ABOUT THE GAS COUPONS. YOU PROBABLY LEFT THEM AT HOME ON THE DRESSER.

BUT, GEE, MOTHER, I DON'T REMEMBER TAKING THEM OUT OF MY BAG.

WE HAVE TO HAVE THE LICENSE PLATES THAT THOSE GAS COUPONS WERE ISSUED TO— H'M, LET'S SEE— THE BROW SAID 27A60.

THERE'S A COOL BREEZE BLOWING IN. I THINK I'LL WALK UP TO THE CAR AND GET MY SWEATER.

BRING MY JACKET, TOO, WILL YOU, TESS?

HERE, WE ARE— 27A60. WITH THIS BOLT CUTTER, THEY'LL BE OFF. TOOT SWEET.

27A60

DICK TRACY

27A60

WELL, THAT'S NUMBER ONE. NOW FOR THIS FRONT PLATE.

BEACH

HEY! YOU! WHAT ARE YOU DOING TO MY LICENSE PLATES?

QUIET, SISTER, BEFORE I GET RECKLESS WITH THIS BOLT CUTTER.

WHY, YOU— **HELP!**

DRUGS

DICK TRACY

THOSE ARE MY LICENSE PLATES POLICE!

BEACH

NOW, TO PICK UP THE BROW.

DRUGS

DICK TRACY

IT'S DOC, AT LAST!

I HAD TO SLUG THE DAME, BUT I GOT THE PLATES.

BREEZE TAKES THE TOWEL

AS THE BROW RUNS TO THE CAR, THE TOWEL IS BLOWN FROM HIS HEAD.

WHAT'S UP, ED?

YE GODS! THAT GUY WITH THE TOWEL OVER HIS HEAD! WHY, HE HAS NO EARS! LOOK!

FIFTEEN MINUTES LATER

I WONDER WHAT'S KEEPING TESS, JEAN?

GOSH, MRS. TRUEHEART, SHE SHOULD BE BACK BY NOW.

DICK TRACY

TESS— —OH, TESS!

OH-H

— MY HEAD!

AS THE DOC'S CAR GLIDES ALONG THE BOULEVARD, THE BROW DRESSES.

ARE YOU ALL SET FOR A LONG TRIP, DOC?

YEAH, BROW, BUT I WANT TO STOP AT THE FIRST SECLUDED SPOT AND PUT ON THOSE OTHER PLATES.

I BROUGHT ALL OF OUR CLOTHES AND BELONGINGS THEY'RE IN THE BACK SEAT.

SIXTY GALLONS. THAT OUGHT TO TAKE US AT LEAST 7 OR 8 HUNDRED MILES.

DICK TRACY

AS DOC AND THE BROW SPEED DOWN THE HIGHWAY, THE STOLEN LICENSE NUMBERS ARE ALREADY BEING BROADCAST TO ALL SQUAD CARS

I'M SURE THOSE WERE THE STOLEN NUMBERS, JOE. STEP ON IT!

I'M INCLINED TO AGREE WITH YOU, GRANT, BECAUSE AS THEY SAW US TURN, THAT DRIVER STEPPED ON IT.

YEP, HERE THEY COME! THE BROW'S SAFE UNDER THAT FARM IMPLEMENT TARPAULIN. BUT ME— I'VE GOT TO TAKE IT ON THE CHIN.

YE GODS! I DIDN'T THINK ANYBODY SAW ME HIDE HERE.

THE HIGHWAY

DICK TRACY

YEP, IF THE RAIN STAYS AWAY I OUGHT TO HAVE THE REST OF THOSE SOYBEANS PLANTED BY DARK

ULP!?? ?

MEANWHILE, DOC IS DOING HIS BEST TO GET AWAY FROM THE HIGHWAY OFFICERS

HE'S DOING ALMOST 85 THOSE OLD CIVILIAN TIRES WON'T STAND MUCH OF THAT.

DICK TRACY

AT 85 MILES AN HOUR, TRAGEDY STRIKES THE BROW'S FLEEING ACCOMPLICE, DOC!

SSS POP!

HE'S BLOWN A TIRE!

BE ON YOUR WAY, MISTER. WE DON'T ALLOW BUMS SLEEPING AROUND OUR PROPERTY.

AND BACK DOWN THE ROAD

YEAH? WELL THIS BUM IS GOING TO TAKE YOUR TRACTOR

AND TAKE YOUR HAND OFF THAT TRACTOR THROTTLE.

BANG BANG

WHAT? NOW, LOOK HERE THAT'S GOING TOO FAR! I'VE A GOOD MIND TO—

I'M TAKING THE TRACTOR.

BANG

DICK TRACY

YE GODS! HE HIT THAT CULVERT WITH TERRIFIC IMPACT

LOOKS LIKE THERE'S ONLY ONE OF 'EM. THE HEADQUARTER'S FLASH SAID THERE WERE TWO!

YEAH, ROUTE 62 AT GOLF ROAD! WE'VE FOUND YOUR STOLEN LICENSE PLATES ALL RIGHT

AND ON A GRAVEL SIDE ROAD

IT'S GETTING DUSK. H'M? LOOKS LIKE A BIG BARN, BUT WHY ALL THOSE LIGHTS?

DICK TRACY

THERE ARE NO LIGHTS ON THIS TRACTOR—I'VE GOT TO GO ON AFOOT.

SUMMER THEATER

LOVE IN HASTE Starring The HICKORY BEAM PLAYERS

I'M IN LUCK! IT'S A BARN THEATRE! PEOPLE! CROWDS! IT'S A BREAK!

AND ACROSS THE FIELDS ON THE MAIN HIGHWAY

BUT I TELL YOU THERE'S JUST ONE OF 'EM, TRACY.

YEAH? THEN THE OTHER ISN'T FAR AWAY

DICK TRACY

LADIES AND GENTLEMEN, THE HICKORY BEAM PLAYERS PRESENT, "LOVE IN HASTE," A COMEDY IN 3 ACTS THANK YOU.

AT LEAST, I'M THIS FAR WITHOUT THE COPS ON MY HEELS. H'M? WELL, I CAN'T STAND HERE.

BACKSTAGE! THE PLAY IS ON — NOW, WHAT?

DICK TRACY

FINDING THE WOUNDED FARMER, THE POSSE, HEADED BY DICK TRACY, TRAILS THE TRACTOR ON WHICH THE BROW ESCAPED.

TRACY SAID TO STAY HERE BY THE TRACTOR. HE AND PATTON HAVE GONE OVER TO THE BARN THEATRE.

WE JUST CAME UP IN TIME TO HEAR THE ANNOUNCEMENT THAT SOME GAS COUPONS HAD BEEN FOUND. MAY I SEE THEM?

OH, YES, MR. TRACY.

NOW, I'M IN FOR IT. WHAT A BONER! THEY SLIPPED OUT OF MY SHIRT POCKET AND THROUGH THAT CRACK.

AT THE END OF THE SHOW

YES, MR. TRACY, WE FOUND THEM LYING RIGHT THERE ON THAT TABLE, AFTER THE FIRST ACT.

THEY'RE TESS' GAS COUPONS, ALL RIGHT.

DICK TRACY

MISS TRUEHEART MIGHT HAVE BEEN UP HERE ON STAGE BEFORE THE SHOW

NO. I HAPPEN TO KNOW SHE'S NOT ANYWHERE NEAR HERE.

THESE COUPONS WERE DROPPED OR LEFT HERE BY SOMEONE ELSE.

AS THE BROW LIES TENSE, HARDLY DARING TO BREATHE, HIS FOOT MOVES EVER SO SLIGHTLY! PARTICLES OF DRIED FIELD MUD LOOSEN FROM HIS SHOE

CLICK CLICK

DICK TRACY

WHAT DID YOU SEE, TRACY?

PIECES OF DIRT AND DUST CAME DOWN FROM THAT LOFT.

IF YOU'RE UP THERE, BROW, COME DOWN NOW!

I HEARD SOMETHING TRACY.

COME DOWN, BROW, OR I'M COMING UP!

DICK TRACY

THE BLOOD'S GETTING IN **MY EYES!** I CAN'T SEE —BUT I'VE GOT TO KEEP GOING.

MURPHY SAID HE HEADED DOWN THE GRAVEL SHORT CUT TOWARD CRYSTAL LAKE.

IN HIS HELPLESS CONDITION, THE BROW LOSES CONTROL OF THE STATION WAGON. IT LEAPS ACROSS A GRASSY STRIP BESIDE THE ROAD AND INTO A PASTURE

I CAN'T SEE —

STILL KEEPING ITS UPRIGHT POSITION, IT DROPS COMPLETELY OUT OF SIGHT INTO AN OLD **ABANDONED GRAVEL PIT.**

DICK TRACY

UNABLE TO SEE BECAUSE OF BLOOD, THE BROW MERELY TURNS OFF THE IGNITION AS THE STATION WAGON LEAPS INTO THE GRAVEL PIT!

TOO WEAK TO CARE WHAT HAPPENS NEXT, THE BROW LIES VERY STILL AND QUIET AS THE LAST OF THE POLICE CARS SPEEDS BY

POLICE CAR

THE BROW

BY THE WAY, LET US TAKE A LOOK AT THIS OLD GRAVEL PIT. ITS LENGTH IS ABOUT A MILE. AND AT THE FURTHER END STANDS A SMALL SHACK

STARING FROM A WINDOW OF THIS SHACK JUST NOW IS A PAIR OF EYES, THE OWNER OF WHICH IS THE **ONLY** WITNESS TO THE ACCIDENT.

DICK TRACY

SCENE: HOSPITAL ROOM IN A SMALL TOWN NEAR THE BARN THEATRE.

THEY'VE WITHDRAWN THE LIGHTNING ROD FROM HIS SHOULDER AND GIVEN HIM SHOTS.

WELL, PAT, OLD BOY, WHAT ABOUT THE BROW?

THE BROW AND THE STATION WAGON **JUST DISAPPEARED.**

YES, SIR. TRESPASSING! THAT'S WHAT IT IS! TRESPASSING!

DRIVING INTO MY PROPERTY WITHOUT PERMISSION. EVEN THE OWNER OF A GRAVEL PIT HAS GOT RIGHTS! I'LL **SHOW 'EM.**

THE BROW

DICK TRACY

I SAY, IN THERE — **DO YOU KNOW** YOU'RE TRESPASSING?

HEY, IN THERE — **HEY!** THIS CAR'S ON MY PROPERTY.

PLEASE — HELP ME — I—I **NEED** HELP!

AH! A **MAN!**

DICK TRACY

BUT TRACY, IT'S TRUE. THE BROW AND THE STATION WAGON **JUST DISAPPEARED!**

HONESTLY, I NEVER BELIEVED IN THE SUPERNATURAL BEFORE — BUT THIS BROW—

YOU SEE, TRACY, RIGHT AFTER WE LEFT THE THEATRE BARN—

EASY! I'M GETTING YOU OUT.

COMPANIONSHIP HAS COME TO GRAVEL GERTIE.

DICK TRACY

CARRYING THE BROW TO HER SHACK, THE FEMALE FIGURE ADMINISTERS FIRST AID

YES, GRAVEL GERTIE'S LONELY DAYS ARE OVER. AT LAST, SHE HAS A **MAN**.

THAT COBWEB AND SOOT POULTICE WILL STOP THE BLEEDING OF YOUR WOUNDS AND ALSO HEAL THEM.

AN OLD MAMMY THAT WORKED FOR MY MOTHER YEARS AGO SHOWED ME THAT REMEDY AND IT WORKED ON MY ARM WHEN I CUT IT IN THE SAWMILL.

THERE'S ONLY ONE THING, MY DARLING — THAT SOOT WILL DISCOLOR THE SCARS! THE SCARS WILL BE BLACK. — VERY BLACK.

DICK TRACY

WHEN MY HUSBAND SOLD THE GRAVEL RIGHTS TO OUR FARM YEARS AGO, LITTLE DID I DREAM HE WOULD BACK HIS CAR INTO THE GRAVEL PIT AND **DIE**.

ALL THESE 30 YEARS I HAVE WAITED — BUT NOW — ONCE AGAIN — I **HAVE** A MAN.

I SHALL WASH THESE BLOOD STAINS FROM MY COUCH AND FLOOR. I SHALL MAKE MY ENTIRE ABODE OVER — FOR YOU AND ME, WHO ARE STARTING LIFE ANEW — TOGETHER.

W-WH-WHERE AM I?

LISTEN, I MAY BE LAID UP — BUT I GIVE YOU GUYS **JUST 24 HOURS** TO FIND THAT **STATION WAGON AND THE BROW**. NOW GET BUSY.

YES, SIR, TRACY.

YES, SIR.

DICK TRACY

WHERE AM I? — I CAN'T **SEE!** WHAT HAPPENED?

PATIENCE, MY DARLING, YOU ARE IN GOOD HANDS! — VERY GOOD HANDS, MY SWEET.

LET US ONCE AGAIN LOOK AT THE STATION WAGON THE BROW SO RECENTLY DROVE INTO THE GRAVEL PIT. IS THAT A TINY WISP OF **SMOKE** WE SEE RISING FROM IT?

YES, WHILE THE CAR DID REMAIN UPRIGHT, THE IMPACT OF THE DROP HAS DISLODGED THE BATTERY FROM ITS MOUNTING UNDER THE HOOD. IT SHORT-CIRCUITS, AND THE CABLE INSULATION CATCHES FIRE.

GOSH, TRACY'S SORE ABOUT THE BROW'S ESCAPE! I'M AFRAID WE'RE IN FOR IT, PATTON.

YEAH — WE'RE GOING BACK TO THAT THEATRE BARN AND FIGURE THIS THING OUT FROM <u>THE</u> BEGINNING.

DICK TRACY

JUST A SONG AT TWILIGHT — ♪ ♪ ♪ WHEN THE LIGHTS ARE LOW.

WHAT DID YOU SAY YOUR NAME IS?

GRAVEL GERTIE, MY SWEET, BUT — JUST CALL ME GERTIE.

YOUR VOICE IS SOFT AND LOW. ARE YOU YOUNG?

WHAT DO YOU THINK, MY DARLING? HERE HOLD MY SOFT HAIR IN YOUR HAND

AND AT THE OTHER END OF THE GRAVEL PIT

PATTON, YOU'RE RIGHT. IT IS THE STATION WAGON.

YE GODS! THE BROW'S BEING BURNED ALIVE.

DICK TRACY

BUT — I'M ALL RIGHT, DOCTOR. I SEE NO REASON FOR STAYING IN BED.

YOU'RE RIGHT, TRACY, YOUR WOUND IS HEALING NICELY AND EXERCISE WON'T HURT.

WATCH OUT, PATTON. DON'T GET BURNED

YOU'RE RIGHT, DAVE, THERE'S NOBODY IN THERE.

THE BROW MUST HAVE JUMPED OUT BEFORE THE CAR WENT OVER THE EDGE, PATTON.

YEAH? H'M! STAY HERE, DAVE, AND KEEP WATCH. I'M GOING BACK AND REPORT TO TRACY.

THAT'S IT — SLEEP, MY DARLING! SLEEP AND RELAX WHILE GRAVEL GERTIE WATCHES OVER YOU. JUST DREAM AND REST.

Z Z Z Z Z Z

DICK TRACY

THANK GOODNESS, YOU'RE ABLE TO BE UP, TRACY. I HARDLY EXPECTED THIS.

WELL, I CAN'T GET INTO ANY FIST FIGHTS, PAT, BUT MY SHOULDER IS A LOT BETTER.

SUPPOSE I TOLD YOU THE BROW DROVE THE STATION WAGON OVER THE EDGE OF A GRAVEL PIT, SET IT AFIRE AND THEN DISAPPEARED?

I SHOULD GIVE YOU A BY-LINE ON PAGE ONE FOR BEING OUR STAR REPORTER — IF I WAS RUNNING A NEWSPAPER.

WELL — THERE'S THE BLOOD-SPATTERED SEAT CUSHION. TRACY MAY BE INTERESTED IN THAT.

DRINK TO ME ONLY WITH THINE EYES ♪ ♪ AND I WILL PLEDGE WITH MINE.

BUT I TELL YOU, TRACY, THIS OLD GIRL, GRAVEL GERTIE, IS A RECLUSE SHE WOULDN'T HARBOR THE BROW

NEVERTHELESS, THESE TWO GRAY HAIRS THAT WERE HANGING ON A THISTLE NEAR THE BURNING STATION WAGON BELONGED TO SOMEBODY

SHALL I KICK THE DOOR IN?

NO WAIT A MINUTE.

I HAVE MY SKELETON KEY!

EXCUSE US FOR INTRUDING, BUT —

— BUT WHAT?

DICK TRACY

PAT OUGHT TO BE BACK ANY MINUTE WITH THE COMPARISON TEST REPORT ON THOSE HAIRS. I FEEL POSITIVE GRAVEL GERTIE IS HIDING THE BROW IN HER HOUSE

ONCE WE KNOW SHE'S INVOLVED, WE'LL TEAR THAT SHACK APART. AH! I SEE CAR LIGHTS COMING DOWN THAT SIDE ROAD, NOW.

BUT I WON'T LET YOU GO! I LOVE YOU, BROW. I LOVE YOU.

UNHAND ME, WITCH!

WATCH OUT—THE LAMP!

DICK TRACY

WHAT HAPPENED? THE OLD DAME'S SHACK'S AFIRE!

—AND I SEE SOMEONE RUNNING. IT MUST BE THE BROW.

MY HAIR! MY BEAUTIFUL HAIR! IT'S ALL BURNED OFF!

TRACY! WHERE ARE YOU, TRACY?

WHAT PAT DOESN'T KNOW IS THAT IN THE EXCITEMENT, TRACY SPOTTED THE BROW ESCAPING THROUGH THE UNDERBRUSH AND TOOK AFTER HIM.

IF ONLY I HADN'T KNOCKED THAT LAMP OVER!! I COULD HAVE STEPPED OUT OF THERE WITHOUT THE COPS SEEING ME—OW-OW.

DICK TRACY

I WENT INTO BOTH ROOMS —TRACY ISN'T IN THERE! THANK HEAVEN!

BUT WHERE IS HE? —SO YOU WERE HIDING THE BROW, EH?

HE-HE WAS SO HANDSOME.

GRANNY, YOU'RE GOING TO STICK WITH ME. WE'LL BE WANTING YOU.

WHO, ME?

I'M SURE HE CAME OUT IN THIS CLEARING —BUT WHERE IS HE? H'M? WHAT'S THIS

DICK TRACY

AH— I SEE WHAT THIS IS — IT'S AN ELECTRIC CATTLE FENCE! THAT'S THE CONTROL BOX

THAT MECHANISM BREAKS THE CIRCUIT EVERY SECOND OR SO TO SAVE THE BATTERY.

BUT— I'M FORGETTING THE BROW — HUH?? WHAT'S THIS?

THAT WIRE MOVED! AND I THOUGHT I HEARD A GRUNT! CAN IT BE OUR FRIEND THE BROW ISN'T ACQUAINTED WITH ELECTRIC FENCES?

DICK TRACY

SO YOU GOT A **TASTE** OF THAT ELECTRIC FENCE, EH, BROW? **COME OUT OF THERE!**

BANG BANG

DON'T SHOOT ME — DON'T KILL ME — PLEASE — **DON'T KILL ME!**

I WAS ONLY DOING THAT TO FLUSH YOU OUT OF THERE. **NOW** YOU AND I ARE GOING TO HAVE A **PRIVATE CHAT**.

BUT- BUT

I-I THOUGHT I RAN A LIGHTNING ROD THROUGH YOUR SHOULDER. **HOW** CAN YOU FIGHT?

I'LL SHOW YOU, BROW.

DICK TRACY

BROTHER, YOU'D BETTER START WORRYING 'CAUSE I'M GOING TO PUT ANOTHER WRINKLE IN THAT BROW!

STAND UP! I'M **NOT THROUGH** WITH YOU, YET —

WHEN THAT ELECTRIC FENCE GETS TOO HOT- GET UP — I'VE **GOT** ANOTHER ONE HERE—

CLKK CLKK

DICK TRACY

THEY'RE COMING IN! THEY'VE **GOT THE BROW!** THE RADIO ROOM JUST HANDED ME A FLASH FROM PATTON.

WHAT DO YOU MEAN, 'THEY'RE COMING? THEY'RE HERE **NOW**.

GO EASY WITH HIM, BOYS, HE DOESN'T FEEL MUCH LIKE TALKING.

WHAT AN ASSORTMENT, TRACY! **WHO** IS THE — ER —GIRL FRIEND?

WHAT? YOU MEAN TO TELL ME YOU DON'T KNOW GRAVEL GERTIE?

BREATHLESS MAHONEY, AND B.O. PLENTY

1945

BREATHLESS MAHONEY AND B. O. PLENTY

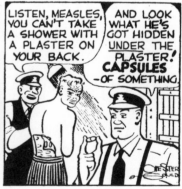

BREATHLESS MAHONEY AND B. O. PLENTY

DICK TRACY

DICK TRACY

DICK TRACY

DICK TRACY

DICK TRACY

BREATHLESS MAHONEY AND HER **MOTHER**— —WHAT CONNIVERS!

YES, BREATHLESS, ALTHOUGH YOU NEVER MET HIM, SHAKY WAS YOUR STEPFATHER.

HE PUT ALL HIS CASH IN A STRONGBOX IN **MY** NAME, BUT HE KEPT THE KEYS IN **HIS** LEFT SHOE.

KEYS BEHIND LINING

THANK GOODNESS ALL THIS HAPPENED WHILE I WAS AWAY AT SCHOOL. I COULD <u>NEVER</u> HAVE CALLED SHAKY DADDY.

YOU'RE RIGHT, TRACY! HER NOTEBOOK **IS** BLANK. EVERY PAGE OF IT. SHE'S **NO** REPORTER.

SHE **INSISTED** ON THE LEFT SHOE— THAT'S THE PART I'M TRYING TO FIGURE. WHY THE LEFT SHOE?

DICK TRACY

YES, BREATHLESS DARLING, TODAY WE SHALL GO TO THE STRONGBOX.

YOU SEE, WHEN I MARRIED SHAKY I KNEW HE HAD MONEY— BUT I DIDN'T KNOW HE GOT IT BY **EXTORTION**

BUT SINCE HE KEPT THE KEYS TO THE STRONGBOX WHICH WAS IN <u>YOUR</u> NAME, WHY DIDN'T YOU TELL THE VAULT COMPANY YOU'D <u>LOST</u> YOUR KEYS AND ASK FOR ANOTHER SET.

BECAUSE HE SAID IF I DID HE WOULD INVOLVE ME IN **EVERY CROOKED DEAL** HE EVER PULLED! HE EVEN THREATENED TO **KILL** ME.

·POOR MOTHER.

DICK TRACY

SAFE DEPOSIT VAULTS

WELL, MRS. MAHONEY, WE HAVEN'T SEEN YOU FOR SOME TIME.

NO, I'VE BEEN AWAY.

THREE-NINETY-SEVEN. **HERE** WE ARE.

PERHAPS YOU'D LIKE TO USE ONE OF THE PRIVATE ROOMS WITH A TABLE. IT'S MORE COMFORTABLE.

THANK YOU.

IS IT FULL? —OR IS IT EMPTY?

DICK TRACY

OPENING THE STRONGBOX! BREATHLESS MAHONEY AND HER MOTHER ARE BOTH BREATHLESS WITH ANTICIPATION.

THERE YOU ARE.

IS HE GONE?

YES, YES! OF COURSE, MOTHER.

CLICK

NOW, MY DEAR—PERHAPS YOU REALIZE <u>WHY</u> I INSISTED ON BRINGING MY KNITTING BAG.

BREATHLESS MAHONEY AND B. O. PLENTY

DICK TRACY

As breathless and her mother fight over who is to carry the knitting bag, Mrs. Mahoney's wrist watch falls off.

THANK YOU, MR. TRACY. NOW, SHALL WE GO?

YES, WE'LL BE LATE FOR THE INQUEST.

THAT INSCRIPTION! SO SHE WAS SHAKY'S FOURTH WIFE! AND BREATHLESS, HIS STEPDAUGHTER! I'M BEGINNING TO SEE THE LIGHT.

IF I LET HER OUT OF MY SIGHT, IT'LL BE THE LAST OF MY 50,000 DOLLARS.

I DON'T DARE LET HER HAVE THE BAG OR SHE'LL SKIP FOR SURE.

DICK TRACY

THE INQUEST WILL BE HELD IN THE ROOM AT THE END OF THE HALL, LADIES. RIGHT THIS WAY.

POWDER ROOM

WHAT'S THE MATTER? DON'T YOU TRUST YOUR OWN DAUGHTER?

YOU BET I DON'T! DID YOU THINK YOU COULD SHAKE ME? HAH!

WELL, BREATHLESS, DEAR, THERE ARE NO EXIT WINDOWS OR DOORS IN HERE. DON'T YOU THINK WE'D BETTER ATTEND THE INQUEST.

DICK TRACY

I THINK THAT WILL BE ALL, MISS MAHONEY. THANK YOU FOR YOUR TESTIMONY AS TO HOW YOU DISCOVERED SHAKY'S BODY.

I'VE GOT TO FIND OUT WHAT'S IN THAT KNITTING BAG! NEITHER WOMAN WILL LET GO OF THE HANDLE!

WELL, IF YOU'RE THROUGH WITH BREATHLESS, MR TRACY, I THINK WE SHALL RETURN HOME

OH, THAT'S TOO BAD. I WAS GOING TO ASK YOU BOTH TO HAVE LUNCH WITH ME.

BUT PERHAPS BREATHLESS WILL JOIN ME I'LL SEE THAT SHE GETS HOME LATER.

OH WELL, ALL RIGHT, MR. TRACY, WE'LL BOTH HAVE LUNCH WITH YOU! —BOTH OF US.

DICK TRACY

WE ENJOYED THE LUNCH SO MUCH, MR. TRACY. GOOD-BYE, NOW.

GOODBYE, BREATHLESS. GOODBYE, MRS. MAHONEY

ECKERT, YOU AND I ARE GOING TO THE MAHONEY APARTMENT ALLEY ENTRANCE, AND DO A LITTLE SNOOPING WE'RE GOING TO FIND OUT WHAT'S IN THAT BAG

POLICE

SO, MY LOVELY, YOU THOUGHT YOU'D GET A CHANCE TO RUN AWAY WITH MY MONEY, EH?

I DON'T CARE WHAT YOU SAY. I'M ENTITLED TO HALF.

YOU'RE WHAT? THAT'S MY MONEY! AND I WON'T EAT OR SLEEP TILL YOU ADMIT YOU WERE TRYING TO BE A LITTLE THIEF.

I'M YOUNGER THAN YOU AND I'VE GOT MORE ENDURANCE! YOU'LL FALL ASLEEP FIRST— AND WHEN YOU DO—

BREATHLESS MAHONEY AND B.O. PLENTY

DICK TRACY

THE CONTEST OF WHO CAN STAY AWAKE LONGER, AND THUS MAKE OFF WITH THE $50,000, HAS TAKEN A MOST TRAGIC TURN.

OH – MY HEART – MY **HEART**

THE BOTTLE WAS HALF FULL. YOU TOOK **EVERY** STAY AWAKE TABLET IN THE BOTTLE. YOUR GREEDINESS MAY KILL YOU.

WATER— GIVE ME-- --GLASS OF-- --WATER-- OH, THE PAIN. -MY HEART!

YOU ALWAYS HAD A WEAK HEART, MOTHER. YOU SHOULD HAVE KNOWN BETTER THAN TO TAKE SO MUCH OF THIS DRUG. **THIS IS TOO BAD.**

IT WAS A CONTEST TO SEE WHO WOULD STAY AWAKE LONGER. OKAY, I WIN

---CALL --DOCTOR--

DICK TRACY

INSPECTING THE REAR OF THE MAHONEY APARTMENT, DICK TRACY DISCOVERS SHAKY'S SHOE BREATHLESS TOOK AS A SOUVENIR LYING ON A GARBAGE CAN

YES, YOU CAN SEE THE IMPRESSION OF KEYS ON THE COUNTER.

STRONG BOX KEYS, WITHOUT A DOUBT! ALL OF WHICH **SETTLES** THE QUESTION OF WHAT WAS IN THE KNITTING BAG.

WHAT ARE YOU DOING NOW, MR. TRACY.

WHILE WE'RE HERE, VINCE, WE MIGHT AS WELL PLAY SCAVENGER A LITTLE FURTHER AND SEE WHAT ELSE WE CAN FIND.

A HEART ATTACK BROUGHT ON BY STAY-AWAKE DRUGS! WELL, SHE DID IT HERSELF! IT WASN'T MY FAULT. TA, TA, MOTHER.

THE $50,000

DICK TRACY

BELIEVING HER MOTHER DYING, BREATHLESS PREPARES TO SKIP — WITH THE KNITTING BAG OF MONEY.

I WON'T TAKE ANY CLOTHES WITH ME. I'LL GO JUST AS I AM.

BUT AS THE FIRST SHOCK OF THE HEART ATTACK SUBSIDES, MRS. MAHONEY GAINS HER SENSES.

BESIDES, WITH $50,000 I CAN BUY ALL THE NEW CLOTHES I WANT.

SLOWLY THE OLDER WOMAN'S HAND FUMBLES IN THE BED-TABLE DRAWER.

BREATHLESS.

DON'T GO **THROUGH** THAT **DOOR!**

DICK TRACY

DON'T MOVE ONE STEP, MY LOVELY! NOT ONE STEP!

THE $50,000

DAUGHTER OR NO DAUGHTER — IF YOU MOVE ONE INCH TOWARD THAT DOOR I'LL FIRE.

YOU WOULDN'T **DARE.**

SO LONG MOTHER.

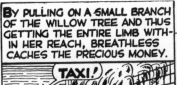

DICK TRACY

THERE YOU ARE. I'M SORRY, MISS, BUT I MUST REPORT GUNSHOT WOUNDS. YOUR NAME, PLEASE?

JOAN MARTIN.

JOAN MARTIN? HM?? HELLO— HELLO, OPERATOR. HELLO.

CLICK CLICK CLICK

MIGHTY 7TH WAR LOAN

Reg. U. S. Pat. Off.: Copyright, 1945, by The Chicago Tribune.

NURSE, MY DIRECT OUTSIDE WIRE HAS BEEN BROKEN! THE GIRL IS GONE! CALL POLICE HEADQUARTERS!

DICK TRACY

WHERE DO YOU WANT US TO START PRUNING TREES, HERMAN?

VALLEY TREE SURGEONS

OH, IT DOESN'T MAKE MUCH DIFFERENCE MRS. VAN HOOSEN WANTS THEM ALL TRIMMED.

Reg. U. S. Pat. Off.: Copyright, 1945, by The Chicago Tribune.

OKAY, THEN I GUESS WE MIGHT AS WELL START WITH THE WEEPING WILLOW TREE.

DON'T DISTURB THE BIRD'S NEST, JAKE —THE OLD LADY'S CRAZY ABOUT BIRDS.

YEAH, WE WON'T TOUCH THAT NEST.

DICK TRACY

MR. TRACY WILL BE RIGHT OVER. HE FELT PUT OUT THAT YOU DIDN'T KEEP THE GIRL HERE.

KEEP HER? SHE RAN OUT ON ME!

DOCTORS NURSES

THAT WILLOW TREE! I'VE GOT TO GET BACK THERE AND GET MY MONEY.

BUS CO.

MIGHTY 7TH WAR LOAN

Reg. U. S. Pat. Off.: Copyright, 1945, by The Chicago Tribune.

THAT'S A SCREWY KIND OF A BIRD'S NEST, JAKE. I THINK I'LL CUT IT DOWN AFTER ALL!

NO SIR! OLD LADY VAN HOOSEN PROBABLY PUT IT UP THERE HERSELF! SHE'D SKIN US ALIVE IF WE TOOK IT DOWN.

WHAT?—THEY'RE—THEY'RE CUTTING OFF THE LIMBS? THEY'LL SEE MY MONEY! I—I'LL—I'LL—

DICK TRACY

THEY'RE REMOVING THE LIMBS THEY CUT OFF THE WEEPING WILLOW. I WONDER IF THEY SAW—?

NO—IT'S STILL THERE! GOOD! GOOD! MY MONEY'S STILL THERE!

AS SOON AS THEY'VE GONE I'LL PULL THE LIMB DOWN AND REMOVE THE BAG, HUH?? BUT HOW CAN I?? THE LIMBS THAT HUNG OVER ARE—

MIGHTY 7TH WAR LOAN

Reg. U. S. Pat. Off.: Copyright, 1945, by The Chicago Tribune.

WELL— LET'S LOAD 'EM IN THE TRUCK AND GET OUT OF HERE.

I'LL GO IN AND GET MRS. VAN HOOSEN TO INSPECT THE TREES BEFORE YOU GO.

DICK TRACY

I CALLED YOU AS SOON AS I COULD. YOU SEE, SHE CUT MY OUTSIDE PHONE LINE.

DOCTOR, THESE THREE WILLOW LEAVES FOUND ON YOUR FLOOR MAY GIVE US SOME HELP.

THEY MUST HAVE CAUGHT IN HER CLOTHES SOME WAY AND THEN DROPPED TO THE FLOOR, WHEN SHE REMOVED HER COAT.

TRACY, WHAT MAKES YOU THINK THOSE WILLOW LEAVES DROPPED FROM BREATHLESS' CLOTHES?

IT SEEMS TO ME THAT THAT TRAIL OF BLOOD FROM THE OLD LADY'S APARTMENT LED BENEATH A WILLOW TREE SOMEWHERE.

IF I CAN GET EMPLOYMENT HERE IT'LL GIVE ME A CHANCE TO GET MY MONEY OUT OF THE WILLOW TREE WITHOUT AROUSING SUSPICION.

THIS WAY, PLEASE! MADAM VAN HOOSEN, HERSELF, HIRES ALL THE HELP.

DICK TRACY

BELIEVE IT OR NOT, MRS. VAN HOOSEN, A YOUNG LADY IS HERE LOOKING FOR A JOB AS MAID. SHALL I SEND HER IN?

BY ALL MEANS, JEEVES!

H'M?? HAVE YOU HAD ANY EXPERIENCE, MY DEAR?

OH, YES, MA'M, BUT I FORGOT TO BRING MY LETTERS OF RECOMMENDATION. —THEY'RE AT HOME IN MY OTHER SUIT.

OH, HANG THE RECOMMENDATIONS. NOW, AS TO SALARY, WHAT DID YOU EXPECT?

I'LL LEAVE THAT TO YOU, MA'M. I KNOW YOU'LL BE VERY FAIR.

THAT GOT THE OLD GIRL. SHE BEAMED FROM EAR TO EAR. OH, WELL, SHE WON'T SEE ME HERE AFTER TONIGHT.

HM? YEP, THE MONEY'S STILL IN THE TREE.

DICK TRACY

WELL, YOU LOOK VERY NICE, MARIE. JEEVES WILL EXPLAIN YOUR DUTIES

THANK YOU, MA'M.

HERMAN, I UNDERSTAND YOU WANTED TO SEE ME THIS MORNING BUT I WAS SLEEPING.

YES, MA'M. I THOUGHT, PERHAPS, YOU'D LIKE TO INSPECT THE TREES SINCE THEY'VE BEEN TRIMMED.

THEY ALL LOOK VERY NICE EXCEPT THE WEEPING WILLOW.

PERHAPS THEY TRIMMED IT TOO CLOSE, MA'M.

HERMAN, WHAT'S THAT HORRID BASKET UP THERE?

BASKET? WHY, MA'M, BELIEVE ME, THIS IS THE FIRST TIME I'VE NOTICED IT.

MY MONEY!

DICK TRACY

SHE SEES IT! SHE'S DISCOVERED THE KNITTING BAG!

BUT SHE CAN'T KNOW WHAT'S IN IT. AND IT'S UP TO ME TO KEEP HER FROM FINDING OUT.

I'M SORRY, MA'M, I DON'T KNOW WHO PUT IT UP THERE.

WELL, GET YOUR PRUNING HOOK. CUT THAT OLD BAG DOWN AT ONCE.

YES, MA'M.

UNDOUBTEDLY THE WORK OF NEIGHBORHOOD KIDS! BAH! UNRULY LITTLE GUTTERSNIPES. IMPS! RASCALS! CUT IT DOWN, HERMAN. CUT IT DOWN!

BREATHLESS MAHONEY AND B. O. PLENTY

DICK TRACY

CAN'T IMAGINE WHO TIED IT UP THERE, BUT IF MRS. VAN HOOSEN WANTS IT DOWN, DOWN IT WILL COME

HM! SEEMS TO BE FULL OF STICKS—PROBABLY TWIGS FROM THE TREE SURGEON'S KNIFE.

WHY, THE—*#★!!~! BREATHLESS, YOU'VE GOT TO GET BUSY.

DICK TRACY

MONEY! MONEY! THOUSANDS OF DOLLARS! —A FORTUNE!

MRS. VAN HOOSEN SAID TO CUT IT DOWN—CUT IT DOWN! SHE SAID IT WAS AN UGLY OLD BAG. NOBODY SAW ME.

AND AT THIS MOMENT ON THE OTHER SIDE OF THE WALL.

YOU'RE RIGHT, TRACY. THE BLOOD SPOTS DO LEAD TO A WILLOW TREE. HERE IT IS.

AS THE GARDENER FRANTICALLY HASTENS TO HIS QUARTERS OVER THE GARAGE, BREATHLESS MAHONEY PONDERS HER NEXT MOVE.

MY MONEY!

DICK TRACY

SO YOU'RE THE CULPRIT WHO'S BEEN TYING STUFF IN MY TREE! NOW, GET DOWN FROM THERE BEFORE I HAVE YOU ARRESTED.

I JUST UNTIED THIS FROM ONE OF THE LIMBS.

OH, REALLY? SO YOU'RE WITH THE POLICE? DEAR ME.

THIS PIECE OF CORD ONCE HELD A KNITTING BAG. TELL ME, MRS. VAN HOOSEN, WHERE IS THAT BAG?!

AND IN THE YARD MAN'S QUARTERS OVER THE GARAGE.

BUT I TELL YOU THIS IS MY MONEY—I FOUND IT! WHAT CLAIM CAN A COMMON MAID—

GARDENER'S YARD SHEARS

DICK TRACY

A KNITTING BAG FULL OF MONEY? THIS IS MOST AMAZING, MR. TRACY. BUT HOW?--WHO--?

I SUPPOSED THAT BAG HAD BEEN TIED IN MY TREE BY PRANKSTERS.

IT CONTAINED AT LEAST 50,000 DOLLARS, MRS. VAN HOOSEN.

AND IN THE GARDENER'S APARTMENT OVER THE GARAGE.

MY MONEY— --MY MONEY!

DICK TRACY

DICK TRACY

DICK TRACY

DICK TRACY

BREATHLESS MAHONEY AND B. O. PLENTY

DICK TRACY

WHEN I STOPPED SUDDENLY, I HEARD THAT PAN BANG AGAINST THE TRUCK. JUST HOW DID **YOU** GET IN HERE?

WELL, YOU SEE, I WAS JUST HITCHHIKING A RIDE DOWNTOWN TO DO SOME SHOPPING —AND—

GONNA BUY A COUPLE OF HANDKERCHIEFS, NO DOUBT. WHY, THERE'S **THOUSANDS** OF DOLLARS THERE.

LISTEN, BABY, I DON'T CARE WHO YOU ARE. OR HOW YOU GOT HERE. BUT I AM INTERESTED IN THAT MAZUMA.

NOW, JUST TELL WETWASH **ALL** ABOUT IT. I THINK **YOU** AND **I** CAN GET TOGETHER.

DICK·TRACY

ALL I KNOW, MA'M, IS THAT I SAW THE MAID GOING UPSTAIRS TO HER ROOM TWENTY MINUTES AGO. SHE WAS CARRYING A ROASTING PAN.

IT'S APPARENT THAT SHE LEFT HER ROOM IN A HURRY. H'M??. HER UNIFORM BEARS SEVERAL SPOTS THAT APPEAR TO BE BLOOD.

ALL RIGHT, WETWASH, YOU'VE GUESSED IT! I AM SORT OF— AVOIDING THE AUTHORITIES.

AND YOU'RE SO YOUNG, TOO.

YOU LOOK LIKE A PRACTICAL GUY—HOW MUCH DO YOU WANT TO KEEP YOUR MOUTH SHUT.

OH, LADY, HOW YOU TALK. WHY, THAT WOULD BE UNETHICAL — THAT WOULD BE UNTHINKABLE!— er-**HOW ABOUT HALF?**

DICK TRACY

I SAID 'I'D GIVE YOU **FIVE HUNDRED** DOLLARS. AND NOT ONE CENT MORE.

WHY, SISTER, THAT PILLOW CASE IS BULGING WITH THOUSAND-DOLLAR BILLS! **I WANT HALF.**

IT'S **FIVE HUNDRED OR NOTHING.**

OKAY, BABE, HAVE IT YOUR WAY.

SLAM!

—YOU SEE, AT THE TIME, SIR, I WAS IN THE BASEMENT HELPING LOAD THE LAUNDRY TRUCK

LAUNDRY TRUCK! WHAT LAUNDRY TRUCK?

IT'S A TEN-MINUTE DRIVE TO THE NEAREST POLICE STATION, AND I'M **GONNA START DRIVING.** THINK FAST, BABY, YOU'VE GOT **TEN MINUTES** TO CHANGE YOUR MIND.

I WON'T GIVE YOU MORE THAN 500!

DICK TRACY

I SAID I'D GIVE YOU **FIVE HUNDRED** DOLLARS —AND NOT A PENNY MORE.

OKAY, THE POLICE STATION'S IN THE **NEXT BLOCK.**

YES, SIR. HERE WE ARE.

NO! WAIT! DON'T STOP! I'LL RAISE THAT TO A **THOUSAND**

WELL, NOW YOU'RE STARTING TO TALK. I WON'T TURN YOU OVER TO THE COPS, BUT I STILL DON'T LIKE YOUR PROPOSITION.

50-50 OR NOTHING!

HE'LL EITHER DO BUSINESS ON MY TERMS OR I'LL TEAR UP EVERY PIECE OF LAUNDRY IN THIS TRUCK. I'LL SHOW HIM

R-RIP

216

BREATHLESS MAHONEY AND B.O. PLENTY

DICK TRACY

IT'S OUT OF GAS! BONE DRY!

WHERE AM I? WHAT CAN I DO? THERE'S AN OLD SHACK—H'M?

THE 50 GRAND

I HEAR A TRACTOR! THAT MEANS THEY HAVE GASOLINE. MAYBE THEY'LL LEND ME SOME.

I'LL KNOCK AT THE FRONT DOOR FIRST AND MAKE UP A STORY FOR THE FARMER'S WIFE. THAT'S MY BEST BET.

DICK TRACY

H'M—? IT SEEMS THERE'S NOBODY IN.

HUH WHO'S THAT—?

WE'VE FOUND IT, ED. THAT'S THE MISSING TRUCK.

I'LL RADIO TRACY.

THEY'RE SEARCHING FOR WETWASH, NOW. THINGS ARE GETTING HOT! I'D BETTER GET INSIDE.

YE GODS! WHAT KIND OF A FAMILY LIVES HERE? WHAT A MESS! THIS PLACE MUST BE RUN BY A BACHELOR.

DICK TRACY

YEAH, THEY FOUND THE LAUNDRY TRUCK ON A SIDE ROAD OUT SOUTHEAST OF TOWN. WE'RE HEADING THERE, NOW.

DID THEY FIND WETWASH? WHAT ABOUT BREATHLESS?

AND IN THE FARMER'S SHACK.

THE SQUAD CAR IS STILL OUT FRONT. I'D BETTER GO OUT THE BACK WAY AND GET AWAY FROM HERE.

THAT FARMER! I WONDER IF HE WOULD—?? H'M? WHY NOT? HE LOOKS AS THOUGH HE COULD USE SOME MONEY.

B.O. PLENTY IS THE NAME, MISS. CAN I BE OF ANY HELP?

DID YOU SAY B.O. PLENTY?

DICK TRACY

THERE'S A THOUSAND DOLLARS. I WANT YOU TO HIDE ME.

HIDE YOU?

WHY, MA'M, THAT'S AWFUL NICE OF YOU. BUT WHERE COULD I HIDE YOU?

IN ONE OF THOSE FURROWS—UNDER THE DIRT.

YOU MEAN YOU WANT B.O. PLENTY TO PLOW YOU UNDER?

WELL, BOYS, HERE WE ARE. WHAT'S THE LATEST?

YES, PLOW ME UNDER!

DICK TRACY

WELL, THERE SHE IS! I PLOWED HER UNDER JUST LIKE SHE ASKED ME TO DO.

BREATHLESS MAHONEY

ARE YOU ALL RIGHT, MISS? CAN YOU BREATHE?

GET AWAY FROM ME YOU DUMBBELL, THE COPS WILL BE HERE ANY MINUTE.

HEY, YOU! COME OVER HERE. WE WANT TO TALK TO YOU.

DICK TRACY

A DETECTIVE, EH? WELL! — MY NAME'S B.O. PLENTY. MAN AND BOY, I'VE LIVED IN THESE PARTS 40 YEARS.

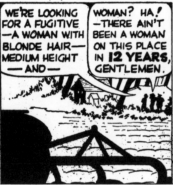

WE'RE LOOKING FOR A FUGITIVE —A WOMAN WITH BLONDE HAIR— MEDIUM HEIGHT —AND—

WOMAN? HA! —THERE AIN'T BEEN A WOMAN ON THIS PLACE IN 12 YEARS, GENTLEMEN.

I'M A BACHELOR— AIN'T HAD A FEMALE ON THIS PLACE SINCE AUNT HATTIE WENT TO HER REWARD IN '33. NO, SIR.

THIS DIRT IS COLD — AND HEAVY. I CAN'T STAND IT HERE VERY LONG.

DICK TRACY

HER TRUCK RAN OUT OF GAS IN FRONT OF YOUR HOUSE. WE FIGURE SHE'S HERE SOMEPLACE. WE'LL HAVE TO SEARCH THE BUILDINGS.

WHY, SHORE. GO AHEAD.

MEANWHILE, PAT, WHOM TRACY HAD SENT BACK ALONG THE TRAIL OF SCATTERED LAUNDRY, MAKES PROGRESS.

WELL, HERE'S ANOTHER TORN SHIRT— AND THERE'S A STREAM.

WHERE AM I?

HUH?

AND BREATHLESS, IN HER GRAVE-LIKE HIDEOUT, DISCOVERS A NEW MENACE.

A SNAKE!

DICK TRACY

NO, YOU WON'T FIND ANY WOMAN ON THIS PLACE, MR. MACY.

THE NAME IS TRACY.

IT'S STARTING TO RAIN.

THERE'S NOBODY IN THE BARN, TRACY.

UGH! THAT SNAKE IS COMING STRAIGHT TOWARD THIS HOLE.

I MUST'NT SCREAM! I CAN'T SCREAM! THEY'LL DISCOVER ME. I MUST CONTROL MYSELF. UGH! I FEEL ITS COLD BODY ON MY FACE.

BREATHLESS MAHONEY AND B.O. PLENTY

DICK TRACY

WELL, B.O. PLENTY, WE CAN'T FIND ANY TRAIL OF THE WOMAN WE'RE AFTER—SO WE'LL LET YOU GET BACK TO YOUR PLOWING.

NO, IT'S RAINING TOO HARD TO PLOW ANY MORE, MR. DACY.

TRACY'S THE NAME.

WON'T YOU COME INSIDE, FELLERS, OUT OF THE RAIN? I'LL STEW UP A POT OF COFFEE FER US.

IT AIN'T MUCH OF A PLACE TO LOOK AT — BUT IT'S HOMEY AND NEAT.

AND BREATHLESS MAHONEY LIES HELPLESS IN THE RAIN-SODDEN FIELD.

DICK TRACY

LOOK, TRACY! SOMEONE'S COMING.

IT'S WETWASH WALLY AND PAT.

THEN HE DID FIND THE LAUNDRY MAN.

THE RAIN IS GETTING HEAVIER.

AND COLDER.

COUGH COUGH.

BREATHLESS STILL PLOWED UNDER

KEEP YOUR EYES ON THIS B.O. PLENTY. HE KNOWS MORE THAN HE'S TELLING.

YEAH?

COME RIGHT IN, GENTLEMEN.

DICK TRACY

AFTER TRACY AND THE POLICE DEPART, B.O. PLENTY GOES INTO THE RAIN-DRENCHED FIELD AND BRINGS UNCONSCIOUS BREATHLESS INTO HIS HOUSE.

THIS COFFEE OUGHT TO FIX HER UP—THAT IS, IF SHE'S STILL ALIVE. CAN'T SAY THAT I DETECTED HER BREATHING WHEN I FETCHED HER IN.

I COULDN'T HARDLY WAIT TILL THEM POLICE FELLERS LEFT—SO I COULD GO OUT AND GET HER. I HID HER SACK OF MONEY IN THE WOODBOX BY THE STOVE. IT'LL BE MINE NOW.

GOSH, SHE'S SO SOFT LOOKING AND PURTY. I-I SORTER HATE TO WAKE HER UP.

DICK TRACY

H'M-M! LOOK AT HER PURTY WHITE CHEEKS

AHEM!

UH-ER-WAL HELLO! — I-I THOUGHT YOU'D GONE BACK TO TOWN, MR. RACY.

TRACY IS THE NAME.

I JUST MADE SOME COFFEE FER YOU. WILL YOU HAVE A CUP?

WHERE DID YOU HAVE 'ER HID, B.O.?

WHO, ME? WH — SHE JEST DROPPED IN. I DON'T KNOW WHO SHE IS.

BREATHLESS MAHONEY AND B. O. PLENTY

DICK TRACY

HERE COMES A **BUS**. (PUFF-PUFF) I'M IN LUCK. I'LL GRAB IT AND LEAVE HER BEHIND.

I'LL GET ON THAT BUS, TOO! I WON'T LET HIM GET AWAY WITH MY MONEY. **HEY—WAIT!**

TRACY, IT'S ME! IT'S **PAT**. I CAME BACK AT 6 O'CLOCK, LIKE YOU SAID.

THEY'VE **POISONED** YOU—. ——! I FOUND THE BOX ON THE STOVE.!—POISON WHEAT IN THE COFFEE GROUNDS. **CAN YOU HEAR ME**, FELLOW?

DICK TRACY

WAKE UP, TRACY. —WAKE UP!

I'D BETTER NOT TRY TO MOVE HIM. I'LL DRIVE BACK TO THE LITTLE VILLAGE OF TINYVILLE AND GET A DOCTOR.

I MADE IT! —THANKS, DRIVER.

YOU'LL NEVER SHAKE ME, B. O. PLENTY. NEVER—.

FARES, PLEASE. I COULD KILL YOU.

DICK TRACY

YOU'D BETTER BRING YOUR SATCHEL, DOC. HE'S BEEN POISONED.

H'M!

HE'S AT THE FARM OF B.O. PLENTY. GOT A DOSE OF POISON WHEAT— RAT EXTERMINATOR.

B.O. PLENTY! MY, MY. I HAVEN'T BEEN ON THAT PLACE IN 30 YEARS

AND ON THE BUS

I ORTA KILLED YOU BACK THERE IN THEM WOODS, YOU FEMALE VIXEN. WHAT DID YE FOLLOW ME FER?

YOU'LL NEVER GET RID OF ME, B.O. PLENTY! I WANT MY MONEY.

AND THE MOTIONLESS FORM OF DICK TRACY REPOSES IN THE FARMHOUSE ROCKING CHAIR, HIS HEAD DROPPING LOWER AND LOWER.

DICK TRACY

HERE WE ARE, DOC ——— AT LEAST HE **ISN'T** DEAD.

LOOK, HIS HAND MOVED!

HE'S TRYING TO **SAY** SOMETHING.

LET ME SEE THE POISON PACKAGE

UH UN-R

H'M! YEAH— WHEAT TREATED WITH NEOTHAL. H'M? GET ME A GLASS OF WATER

WATER?

SNIFF

AND ON THE BUS.

DROWSY— I'M GETTING AWFUL DROWSY.

COFFEE— REMEMBER? YOU FINALLY POURED YOURSELF A CUP OF COFFEE— THAT I MADE.

BREATHLESS MAHONEY AND B.O. PLENTY

DICK TRACY

DICK TRACY

DICK TRACY

DICK TRACY

SCENE: JAIL IN TINYVILLE.

IT'S THE CITY POLICE. THEY'VE GOT TWO OF OUR BOYS. YOU TALK TO HIM.

YEAH, TRACY, WE PICKED UP THESE KIDS IN A JALOPY. THEY'RE OUT OF GAS AND THE CAR'S GOT NO LICENSE PLATES.

YOU SEE, A GIRL ASKED US TO DRIVE HER HERE— THEN SHE DIDN'T PAY US. —WHAT? OH, SHE WAS A BLONDE WITH LONG HAIR AND ——

NOT BAD! A NICE ROOM —LOTS OF MONEY —AND, **OH BOY!** HOW I DITCHED THOSE TWO KIDS. OH, WELL, IT'LL TEACH THEM A LESSON. —AND I SAVED 100 DOLLARS.

DICK TRACY

YOU SAY SHE DITCHED YOU? DIDN'T PAY YOU? I WANT YOU BOYS TO STAY RIGHT THERE. I'M COMING IN TO TALK TO YOU.

TRACY'S VOICE

LET ME TALK TO OFFICER OGDEN, AGAIN.

I GUESS THEY'VE FORGOTTEN ABOUT ME. YEAH— RECKON THEY HAVE.

COUNTY JAIL

BUT YOU **CAN'T** KICK ME OUT OF MY ROOM.

MISTER POOSLE, YOU WERE TWO WEEKS BEHIND IN YOUR ROOM RENT. AND YOU ARE KICKED OUT. **THERE'S YOUR GRIP.**

I'LL SEE THE O.P.A. ABOUT THIS.

DICK TRACY

YES, SIR, I GAVE 'EM THE **SLIP!** WALKED RIGHT OUT OF THAT DANGED JAIL WITHOUT BATTIN' AN EYE.

PUFF PUFF

I WAS TOO QUICK FER 'EM! THEY AIN'T NO FLIES ON B.O. PLENTY. I'M SMART. AND I STILL GOT THE THOUSAND DOLLARS THAT GIRL GAVE ME WHEN I PLOWED HER UNDER.

JONES CLOTHE TIES SHOE

WELL! WHAT CAN I **DO** FOR YOU, B.O.?

WANT TO BUY A NEW SUIT AND A PAIR OF NEW SHOES, CHARLIE. AND I'M **IN** A HURRY.

PAT AND I WILL GO TO THE CITY AND QUESTION THOSE BOYS. MEANWHILE, SHERIFF, GET B.O. PLENTY BACK HERE.

THAT'LL BE EASY. HE COULDN'T STAY AWAY FROM THAT FARM OF HIS IF HE TRIED. HE'S LIVED THERE FOR 50 YEARS.

DICK TRACY

YEAH—THAT **BELT IN THE BACK** IS WHAT I LIKE.

IT'S A NICE GARMENT, B.O.

HOW MUCH DO YOU WANT TO PAY DOWN?

PAY DOWN? **HA!** I'M PAYING **ALL!** —THAT'S WHAT I'M PAYING!

SHERIFF, B.O. PLENTY WAS IN HERE JUST NOW WITH A ROLL THAT'D CHOKE A HOSS —— BOUGHT A NEW SUIT AND SHOES. THOUGHT YOU OUGHT TO KNOW.

HUH?

YEAH, THAT FLYER WILL BE HERE ANY MINUTE AND WHEN IT STOPS AT THAT WATER TANK—

BREATHLESS MAHONEY AND B. O. PLENTY

DICK TRACY

DIDN'T HAVE TIME TO GET A TICKET, MR. CONDUCTOR, BUT I CAN PAY— I CAN PAY!

WHERE TO?

THE CITY? THAT'LL BE THREE SIXTY-TWO.

WHY, SHORE! THERE Y'ARE.

H'M?

BUT I TELL YOU THE LANDLADY KICKED ME OUT OF MY ROOM AND RENTED IT TO A BLONDE. I THINK I SHOULD GO TO THE O.P.A. OR SOMETHING.

YEAH?

THAT'S THE DRUGSTORE WHERE SHE DISAPPEARED, MR. TRACY. SHE— LEFT US FLAT.

YEAH —AND THEN, WHAT?

FAREWELL, MY LOVE. THIS IS THE END.

DON'T LAFF LADY— YOUR DAUGHTER MAY BE RIDING IN TH' CHESTER GOULD

DICK TRACY

THERE! I'VE PUT MY MONEY IN A STRONGBOX. NOW I'M ALL SET.

SAFETY VAULTS

I'VE DITCHED B.O. PLENTY AND DICK TRACY. I'VE GOT MY OWN QUARTERS AND I'M INDEPENDENT! BREATHLESS, DARLING, YOU'RE POSITIVELY BRILLIANT.

H'M, THESE STORE SHOES ARE SHORE TIGHT—AWFUL SNUG.

PORTER— ER DO YOU HAVE A RAZOR BLADE?

WHY, I THINK SO, BOSS.

DICK TRACY

DISCOVERING THAT ONE OF THE DRUGSTORE CLERKS HAS RECENTLY BEEN EVICTED FROM HIS ROOM IN FAVOR OF A BLONDE, DICK TRACY ASKS TO BE SHOWN THE ROOMING HOUSE.

THIS IS THE PLACE, MR. TRACY. IT'S JUST TWO BLOCKS FROM THE DRUGSTORE.

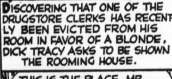

PLEASE, MRS. MIFFINS, DON'T ASK ME ANY QUESTIONS. JUST HIDE ME.

HIDE YOU? WHY SHOULD I HIDE YOU?

HAVING RECOGNIZED TRACY AS HE APPROACHED THE HOUSE, BREATHLESS BECOMES FRANTIC.

PLEASE! WRAP SOME MATERIAL AROUND ME — THE POLICE ARE COMING. PLEASE.

I'LL— I'LL GIVE YOU A THOUSAND DOLLARS— I'LL GIVE YOU TWO THOUSAND DOLLARS.

COME TO THINK OF IT, YOU BRIBED ME WITH A HUNDRED DOLLARS TO GET INTO THIS HOUSE. I DON'T TRUST YOU.

DICK TRACY

THE COPS ARE DOWNSTAIRS. —THEY'LL BE UP HERE ANY MINUTE! AREN'T YOU GOING TO HIDE ME?

AFTER ALL, YOUNG LADY, I'M RUNNING A RESPECTABLE ROOMING HOUSE. I'M NOT GOING TO SHIELD A CROOK

THANKS FOR SHOWING ME THE PLACE.. I'LL SEE YOU— BACK AT THE DRUGSTORE, LATER.

I SHOULD HAVE KNOWN YOU WERE A CROOK— I'M GLAD THE POLICE ARE HERE— IN FACT, I'M GOING TO—

DON'T YOU TOUCH THAT DOOR HANDLE.

PARDON US FOR BREAKING IN HERE— BUT MAY WE SEE WHAT IS HAPPENING TO B.O. PLENTY?

BUT I TELL YOU I HAD A THOUSAND DOLLARS SOMEBODY'S CUT MY POCKET— MY MONEY'S GONE

I OUGHTA BUST YOU IN THE KISSER

BREATHLESS MAHONEY AND B.O. PLENTY

DICK TRACY

WHO HIRED THAT THING OUT FRONT? HE'LL RUIN OUR BUSINESS. HE'S A MONSTROSITY.
I HIRED HIM, BOSS. HELP'S HARD TO GET.

BUT HE LOOKS LIKE A NIGHTMARE!
"PARK MY CAR," HE SAID. NOW, I DON'T SEE ANY PARK.
BIRD CLUB   BIRD CLUB

OF ALL THE PEOPLE IN THIS WORLD! HOW COULD IT BE POSSIBLE THAT I SHOULD RUN INTO B.O. PLENTY!

I NEVER DROVE ONE OF THESE CRITTERS BEFORE. BUT IF OTHER FOLKS CAN DO IT, SO CAN I. I'LL FIND THAT PARK!

DICK TRACY

HE SAID HE WANTS HIS CAR IN A PARK. WELL, FIRST, I'LL PUSH THIS LEVER — THEN — UGH —
BIRD CLUB   BIRD CLUB
SWOOSH

HE'S NEVER DRIVEN BEFORE. WE'LL CRASH! HE'LL KILL US BOTH.

DRIVES A DAD-BLAMED SIGHT DIFFERENT THAN A TRACTOR — WHOA — WHOA!
BUMP

I'M THE COOK. I-I SAW THAT NEW ROOMER RUN ACROSS THE BACK YARD AND CLIMB INTO THE NEIGHBOR'S CAR. — I SAW HER FROM THE KITCHEN.

DICK TRACY

CALL THE CORONER, AND STAY HERE WITH THE BODY, PAT. I'LL CHECK THE COOK'S STORY ABOUT THE CAR ACROSS THE ALLEY.
I SAW HER CLIMB IN.

WHY, YES. YOU SEE, MR. WEST IS THE MANAGER OF THE BIRD CLUB. HE DROVE TO WORK ABOUT AN HOUR AGO.

MEANWHILE
I CAN'T JUST LIE HERE AND BE KILLED. I'VE GOT TO TAKE OVER.

MOVE OVER, YOU MORON! LET ME HAVE THAT WHEEL!
HUH? WHERE DID YOU COME FROM?

DICK TRACY

I SAID, "LET ME HAVE THAT WHEEL!"

WELL, I'LL BE GAL-DARNED IF IT AIN'T THAT BREATHLESS WOMAN THAT PIZONED ME AND TOOK ALL THE MONEY.

WHY, I'VE BEEN WAITING TO GET MY HANDS ON YOU!
STOP IT, YOU BIG MORON. DO YOU WANT TO KILL US BOTH?

LET GO OF MY NECK! WE'LL CRASH! STOP IT, B.O.!

228

DICK TRACY

LET GO OF MY NECK, B.O., AND I PROMISE I'LL GIVE YOU SOME OF THE MONEY.

ALL RIGHT, SISTER, BUT IF YOU FOOL ME THIS TIME, I'LL KILL YOU.

WE'VE GOT TO GET OUT OF THIS HOT CAR. I'LL PARK IT.

LET'S BEAT IT UP HERE TILL WE CAN WORK OUT A PLAN.

HOLD ON A MINUTE! THIS AIN'T NO BANK.

—IT'S THE PUBLIC LIBRARY! BUT WE CAN HIDE OUT HERE FOR A WHILE. STICK THAT NEWSPAPER IN FRONT OF YOUR FACE TILL WE TALK THINGS OVER.

DICK TRACY

TO THINK THAT FATE SHOULD FETCH US ♪ TOGETHER LIKE THIS, BREATHLESS, DARLIN'!

KEEP THAT PAPER IN FRONT OF YOUR FACE. DO YOU WANT US TO BE RECOGNIZED?

HOW MUCH OF MY MONEY DO YOU WANT— YOU PIG?

ALL OF IT— THAT'S ALL ALL OF IT.

AND IF I DON'T GET IT—I'LL TAKE YOU BY YOUR WICKED LITTLE WRISTS AND TURN YOU OVER TO THE FIRST POLICEMAN.

B.O. PLENTY, YOU'RE A CHISELING RAT.

THINK IT OVER, HONEY. I CAN SET HERE IN THE PUBLIC LIBERRY JIST AS LONG AS YOU CAN.

YOU STINKING SNAKE.

DICK TRACY

CHECKING WITH THE NIGHT CLUB OWNER, TRACY DISCOVERS THE MANAGER'S CAR AND B.O. PLENTY HAVE GONE.

YEAH, IT'S A STRONG-BOX RECEIPT, TRACY.

WHEN I SEARCHED BREATHLESS' ROOM I RAN ACROSS IT. THOUGHT I OUGHT TO BRING IT DOWN.

H'M? LOOKS LIKE SHE'S GOT A STRONG BOX AT THE LAKE PORT NATIONAL VAULTS.

MEANWHILE, IN THE DEPOSIT VAULTS WHERE BREATHLESS AND B.O. PLENTY HAVE JUST ENTERED A BOOTH.

SHE SAID HE WAS HER UNCLE.

HE'S CERTAINLY A QUEER LOOKING DUCK; THAT'S ALL I CAN SAY.

YOU DIDN'T SEE ME TAKE THIS CORD OUT OF THE NEWSPAPER FILES IN THE LIBERRY, DID YOU? AHA! WELL, IT'S MY SHOW NOW, SISTER!

BUT YOU SAID—

DICK TRACY

AS B.O. PLENTY TWISTS THE LAC-ING CORD HE FILCHED FROM THE LIBRARY NEWSPAPER FILES, BREATHLESS BECOMES LIMP AND STILL.

THAT'S IT! EASY—NOW! NO NOISE!

SHE MADE ME LEAVE THAT BIG OVERCOAT IN THE LIBRARY, BUT I CAN STUFF THIS IN MY SHIRT.

MY NIECE IS GOING TO BE BUSY IN THERE FOR A WHILE. MEANTIME, I'LL RUN AN ERRAND FER HER TO THE DRUG-STORE.

YES, SIR.

BREATHLESS MAHONEY AND B. O. PLENTY

DICK TRACY

IT WORKED! I GOT THE MONEY. I'M RICH! BUT I'VE GOT TO GET OUT OF HERE.

DEPOSIT BOXES

HEY! WATCH IT!

LAKE PO

WELL, I'LL BE DARNED! WHERE'S HE GOING? HE GOT RED PAINT ALL OVER THOSE WHISKERS.

SAY, THAT OLD GUY'S BLEEDING!

!!~★☆☆ ★☆☆!★ GOTTA FIND A HARDWARE!

U.S.M

DICK TRACY

I'VE GOT TO GET THIS RED PAINT OFF MY BEARD. IN FACT, I'VE GOT TO GET THE BEARD OFF!

HARDWAR

I WANT A RAZOR AND A SET OF HAIR CLIPPERS AND A SHAVING BRUSH AND A PAIR OF SCISSORS.

BACK HERE, PLEASE.

BITS

THAT OLD MAN'S NIECE IS STAYING IN THAT FIRST BOOTH AN' AWFUL LONG TIME JUST TO BE GOING THROUGH A STRONG-BOX.

YEAH, SHE'S BEEN IN THERE ALMOST AN HOUR.

HEY, GEORGE, WAS THAT A GROAN?

NO-SOUNDED LIKE A COUGH.

DICK TRACY

NO, DON'T TOUCH HER — TILL WE CALL THE POLICE.

HER STRONGBOX IS EMPTY!

THAT OLD MAN! HE LEFT ALMOST AN HOUR AGO!

Reg U S Pat Off
Copyright. 1945, by
The Chicago Tribune

NOT A BAD ROOM — BUT PRETTY EXPENSIVE! HOW-SOME-EVER, I CAN AFFORD ANYTHING NOW!

ROOMS $1.50

GOT MYSELF A NEW SUIT, TOO, WHEN I GIT THIS BEARD OFF AND CUT MY HAIR — NOBODY WILL EVER RECOGNIZE B.O. PLENTY.

DICK TRACY

THAT STRONGBOX HUNCH OF YOURS WAS RIGHT, PAT. ONLY WE SHOULD HAVE COME HERE SOONER.

THIS WAY, GENTLEMEN.

SHE'S STILL BREATHING?

THAT LOOKS LIKE A SHOELACE.

Reg. U.S. Pat. Off.
Copyright, 1945, by
The Chicago Tribune.

IT'S BROKEN IN TWO — APPARENTLY UNDER THE STRAIN OF BEING TWISTED.

BREATHLESS, IT DOESN'T PAY.

AND IN HIS ROOM, B.O. PLENTY WORKS FEVERISHLY ON HIS OWN APPEARANCE

THERE! THAT TAKES CARE OF MY HAIR! NOW TO SHAVE.

B.O. Plenty continues at large through various escapades and a jail term until the eventful spring of 1946, when he is rewarded with Sunny Dell Acres by Diet Smith. B.O. then becomes a neighbor of Gravel Gertie, and nature takes it course.

230

MUMBLES

1947

MUMBLES

234

235

MUMBLES

MUMBLES

MUMBLES

WIRE EASTERN AUTHORITIES TO CHECK ALL TRANSPORTATION FROM THE AIRPORT AS WELL AS ALL HOTELS. UNLESS THEY SPLIT UP, FIVE PEOPLE SHOULDN'T BE TOO HARD TO FIND.

AND AT AN EASTERN WATER-FRONT DOCK.

THAT'S MY PRICE. —AND HERE ARE ALL THE PAPERS.

AND HERE'S YOUR DOUGH.

MUMBLES SAID TO GET EVERYTHING READY TO SHOVE OFF. WE'RE GOING SOUTH.

HERE TAK THIS BOTL.

HE SAID HE'D BE BACK IN A FEW MINUTES—AND IF KISS STARTED ANYTHING TO THROW THIS ACID IN HER FACE.

WE FINALLY MADE MUMBLES DIVIDE THE DOUGH **EQUALLY.** GOSH, WHEN WE TOLD HIM WE'D SQUEAL ABOUT KILLING THAT 'HIGHWAY COP—

YEAH, WE'VE GOT HIS NUMBER NOW.

WHAT'VE YOU GOT, MUMBLES?

MORE P'VISIONS.

PROVISIONS?

LET'S SHOVE.

YEAH, LET'S GET THIS TUB GOING.

STOTHA STUFILE TAKARE THIS.

HE SAID TO STOW THAT STUFF. HE WANTS TO TAKE THE OTHER PACKAGE TO HIS CABIN.

A LITTLE PRIVATE REFRESHMENTS, EH, MUMBLES?

PRIVT ERFRESHMENTS, EH? HA! AFTR THIS LIL TRIP NOBODYL SQUEALON MUMBLES. NOBODY!

WHAT DID HE SAY???

11-16-47

OFF TO SOUTHERN WATERS! WOW— MUMBLES, YOU'RE A REAL PAL!

11-17-47

WHAT DID HE SAY?

MUMBLES SAID HE'S GOING TO HIS CABIN. HE'S TIRED.

GOT GET HIS STUFREDY GONBLOW EMALL UP. SHOOK MEDOWN. I'LF IXEM.

CHESTER GOULD

MUMBLES IS **STILL SORE** 'CAUSE WE MADE HIM SPLIT THAT **60 GRAND** EVEN— BUT HE'LL GET OVER IT

SURE, SURE!

244

MUMBLES

246

MUMBLES

248

MUMBLES

PEAR SHAPE

1949

PEAR SHAPE

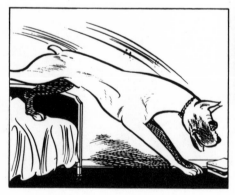

PEAR SHAPE

HALF HOUR LATER— LET'S LIE BACK HERE AWHILE AND WATCH. THAT DOG'S BEEN TRAINED FOR SOMETHING.

HEY, HEAR THAT! SOUNDS LIKE A FIGHT!

I HEAR VOICES AND YELLING.

THAT DOG'S TEARING SOMEBODY APART. LET'S MOVE UP, TRACY.

EASY, SAM. WAIT! LET'S LET THIS DEVELOP. WE MAY LEARN SOMETHING.

A FIGURE RAN OUT OF THE HOUSE.

I HEAR A MOTOR ROARING. A CAR'S PULLING AWAY. LET'S GO.

Reg. U. S. Pat. Off.: Copyright, 1949, by The Chicago Tribune.

HELLO. MUGG! WHAT TH—?? SOMEBODY LOST THE SEAT OF THEIR PANTS, TRACY, LOOK.

THAT LOOKS LIKE A NICE PIECE OF TWEED.

LATER, IN ANOTHER PART OF TOWN. "PEAR-SHAPE" WANTS TO SEE YOU QUICK, AND ON YOUR WAY UP STOP AT THE DRUGSTORE AND GET A BOTTLE OF MERCUROCHROME.

YES, I SAID. MERCUROCHROME! YEAH! "PEAR-SHAPE" GOT BIT BY A DOG!

AND TELL HIM TO STOP AT THE CLEANERS, TOO, AND GET MY OTHER SUIT. I CAN'T GO AROUND THIS WAY.

OKAY, "PEAR-SHAPE."

Reg. U. S. Pat. Off.: Copyright, 1949, by The Chicago Tribune.

YES, SAM, THIS TIME SOMEONE WAS IN HERE.

THAT DOG DOESN'T JUMP THROUGH PLATE GLASS WINDOWS FOR NOTHING, DOES HE?

HE SEEMS TO BE GUARDING THE COOK-STOVE.

HE'S GUARDING SOMETHING AND WE'RE GOING TO TEAR THIS PLACE APART TILL WE FIND IT.

CHESTER GOULD

HOW DO YOU FEEL NOW, "PEAR-SHAPE"?

LISTEN— WERE YOU EVER BIT BY A DOG?

I FIGURED WHEN THAT OLD MAN DIED, SOMEBODY'D TAKE THE DOG.

RIGHT! AND WE CAN'T SEARCH HIS HOUSE AS LONG AS THAT BRUTE'S THERE.

Reg. U. S. Pat. Off.: Copyright, 1949, by The Chicago Tribune.

TO DRILL HIM WOULD AROUSE THE NEIGHBORHOOD.

HEY, "PEAR-SHAPE," HOW ABOUT GAS?

THAT'S DARN FUNNY. EVERY TIME I GO NEAR THE COOKSTOVE, THE POOCH RAVES.

BOW WOW WOW

CHESTER GOULD

PEAR SHAPE

WE DON'T EVEN KNOW WHAT WE'RE LOOKING FOR, SAM.

WHATEVER IT IS, YOU MUST BE GETTING WARM. THE POOCH IS RAISING CAIN.

THERE'S NOTHING IN THESE MEAGER DRESSER DRAWERS BUT A FEW RAGS. WONDER IF THIS HOUSE HAS AN ATTIC..

IT NEVER FAILS! LOOK! WHENEVER I GO NEAR THIS STOVE—

GET A SCREW-DRIVER. LET'S TAKE IT APART.

MASKS? SURE, I KNOW A GUY THAT'S GOT SOME ARMY SURPLUS—

WHAT DO YOU SAY, "PEAR-SHAPE"?

OKAY, GET 2 GAS BOMBS AND 3 MASKS. NO DOG IS GOING TO BITE ME TWICE.

THERE'S NOTHING HIDDEN IN THAT STOVE, TRACY.

THIS IS THE HOT WATER RESERVOIR— AND THERE'S WATER IN IT, SAM.

AND HEY—HOLD IT! THERE'S SOMETHING IN THE WATER—LYING ON THE BOTTOM.

OUT OF THE HOT WATER RESERVOIR OF THE OLD-FASHIONED COOKSTOVE, TRACY AND SAM RETRIEVE A STRANGE OBJECT.

A PIECE OF PIPE?

YEAH, A PIECE OF PIPE—CAPPED AT BOTH ENDS.

IT'S COMING LOOSE, SAM. KEEP IT UP.

A PIECE OF PAPER? THAT OLD MAN CERTAINLY WAS NUTS ABOUT LEAVING MESSAGES IN LITTLE METAL CONTAINERS!

NOW WHAT DOES THIS SAY?

THE PIECE OF PAPER IS BLANK, TRACY.

I WONDER—

WE'RE GOING TO THE LABORATORY, SAM. THAT ECCENTRIC OLD MAN MAY HAVE BEEN AN "INVISIBLE INK" ADDICT.

YEAH?

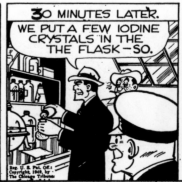
30 MINUTES LATER. WE PUT A FEW IODINE CRYSTALS IN THE THE FLASK—SO.

LET'S SEE WHAT A BIT OF IODINE FUMES WILL DO TO THIS.

260

PEAR SHAPE

LET 'IM UP, MUGG. IT'S OKAY NOW.

MARCH 'EM OUTSIDE!

HEY, THERE'S ANOTHER GAS MASK.

Reg. U. S. Pat. Off.: Copyright, 1949, by The Chicago Tribune.

BOW WOW WOW

THERE WAS A THIRD MEMBER IN THIS GANG, AND THE BOXER'S GOING AFTER HIM. WATCH THOSE TWO, SAM, TILL I GET BACK.

CHESTER GOULD

I SAID, **STAND STILL!** DID YOU THINK I WAS WAS KIDDIN'?

ZING

SO THE THIRD MEMBER TOOK A POWDER, EH? WHAT DO YOU BET HE WON'T BE BACK WITH A BOXER ATTACHED TO THE SEAT OF HIS PANTS?

Reg. U. S. Pat. Off.: Copyright, 1949, by The Chicago Tribune.

AND IN THE BRAMBLES ON THE OTHER SIDE OF THE COTTAGE.

OH, MUGG!

SNIFF SNIFF

HEY, **MUGG!** WHERE **ARE YOU?**

1703

CHESTER GOULD

TWO GUYS—BUT 3 GAS MASKS! COME NOW, TELL SAM WHO THAT **THIRD MEMBER** WAS.

OKAY—WHEN TRACY AND THAT BOXER DOG GET BACK, WE'LL KNOW!

AND SOME DISTANCE FROM THE SHACK, TRACY TRIES HARD TO KEEP UP WITH THE BOXER, "MUGG". HE'S TRACKED HIM TO A PARKED CAR. H'M? HE'S RUNNING AROUND THE CAR.

SNIFF

THE TRAIL LEADS ON, APPARENTLY. MUGG'S GOING UP THE NEXT STREET.

IT'S NO USE, BOY. THIS IS AS FAR AS WE GO. HE BOARDED A STREETCAR.

TEN MINUTES LATER.

SO **THAT'S** WHY YOUR PARTNER COULDN'T DRIVE THE CAR AWAY, EH? **YOU** HAD THE CAR KEYS.

PEAR SHAPE

ONE OF THESE GAS MASKS GIVES US A CLEW TO THE THIRD MAN, HOWEVER. HE HAS **RED** HAIR!

DARNED IF HE DOESN'T, TRACY.

WE'LL CHECK THE OWNERSHIP OF THAT PARKED CAR AFTER WE TAKE THESE BOYS IN.

WE'LL COME BACK LATER WITH MUGG TO LOCATE THOSE JEWELS.

INSIDE, YOU TWO!

WHAT ABOUT MUGG? WHERE'S HE GOING TO RIDE?

HUH?

MUGG! IS **THAT** THE WAY YOU WANT TO RIDE? OKAY, FELLOW.

FROM NOW ON THE UPPER DECK IS RESERVED FOR OUR K-9 CORPS, SAM. LET'S GO.

BUT WHERE IS "PEAR-SHAPE"?

YES, MUGG TRAILED THE THIRD MEMBER TO A STREETCAR LINE—THERE THE TRAIL ENDED—BUT WE HAVE 2 OF THEM.

I WANT MURPHY AND MUNDT TO PICK UP THAT CAR THAT'S PARKED OUT THERE. WE WANT TO TRACE ITS OWNERSHIP.

COME DOWN, MUGG! THIS IS THE END OF THE LINE.

HE LIKES TO RIDE UP THERE.

AND IN ANOTHER PART OF TOWN.

NELLIE—THIS IS "PEAR-SHAPE". YOU'VE GOT TO COME OVER RIGHT AWAY—AND HELP ME MOVE.

I'VE GOT TO GIVE UP MY ROOM, NELLIE. IT ISN'T **SAFE** HERE.

"PEAR-SHAPE," I'VE BEEN TELLING YOU RIGHT ALONG TO MIND YOUR OWN BUSINESS AND FORGET THE RACKETS.

I KNOW! I KNOW! YOU'RE A SMART SECRETARY, NELLIE.

IT ISN'T JUST THAT I'M UP AGAINST THE POLICE, BUT I'M CONTENDING WITH A **DOG! A MAD DOG!**

FROM NOW ON, I'M GOING TO LIVE IN THE **OFFICE.**

REDUCE-U MAIL INSTITUTE

PEAR SHAPE

266

THEY FOUND THE JEWELS, SO **WHAT**? THEY'VE GOT NOTHING ON ME.

COPS HAVE BEEN TRYING TO CRACK THAT CASE FOR A YEAR—BUT IT'S AIRTIGHT! THEY CAN'T—OH, HELLO, NELLIE.

WHY, "PEAR-SHAPE", YOU'RE **EXCITED**.

NO, NO! MY FACE JUST GOT RED WHEN I STOOPED OVER TO BRUSH MY SHOES. GIVE 'EM A LITTLE POLISH, WILL YOU, NELLIE?

TWO PLAIN-CLOTHES MEN ARE HERE, MA'AM, WITH YOUR AUNT'S JEWELS!

WITH MY AUNT'S JEWELS? WHY, SHOW THEM IN, MALLERS.

YES, WE HAVE SOMETHING TO SHOW YOU, MISS WALDO.

LOOK AT THEM CAREFULLY. CAN YOU IDENTIFY THEM?

YOUR MAGNIFYING GLASS, MA'AM.

THANK YOU, MALLERS.

YES—YES, THEY **ARE** HERS. SHE WAS MURDERED FOR THOSE JEWELS—POOR, DEAR AUNTIE.

THE JEWELS FOUND IN THE BONE ARE IDENTIFIED AS BEING THE SAME ONES INVOLVED IN A $500,000 ROBBERY SEVERAL MONTHS AGO. DICK TRACY AND SAM CATCHEM ARE CALLING AT THE HOME OF THE VICTIM.

YES, THOSE ARE MY AUNT MARY'S JEWELS, ALL RIGHT.

AS I RECALL THAT CASE, YOUR AUNT WAS **SHOT** TO DEATH IN HER BEDROOM THE NIGHT OF THE ROBBERY.

MAY WE SEE THAT ROOM?

WHEN WE FOUND HER SHE WAS LYING NEAR THAT WINDOW.

I REMEMBER THE CASE. THE DEPARTMENT WAS UNABLE TO GET A **SINGLE** CLEW.

YES, THAT WAS THE LAST PHOTOGRAPH OF HER.

YOUR AUNT WAS —SHALL WE SAY—A BIT HEAVY?

YES, AUNTIE WAS **VERY** MUCH OVERWEIGHT AND HAD BECOME ALMOST FANATIC IN HER DETERMINATION TO REDUCE.

SHE TRIED DIETING. LATER SHE ENROLLED IN A CORRESPONDENCE COURSE IN REDUCING.

IT WAS QUITE PATHETIC, REALLY.

YEAH, HERE ARE SOME OF THE LESSONS, TRACY.

GOSH, THEY DO ANYTHING BY MAIL, DON'T THEY?

AND AT "PEAR-SHAPE'S" OFFICE. "PEAR-SHAPE," I WISH YOU'D QUIT CARRYING ON A PERSONAL CORRESPONDENCE WITH YOUR PUPILS. JUST STICK TO THE REDUCING LESSONS.

NELLIE, YOU'LL NEVER MAKE A BUSINESS WOMAN. YOU'VE GOT TO FOLLOW UP EVERY POSSIBILITY TO MAKE MONEY.

WHY, RIGHT HERE I'VE GOT ANOTHER DAME THAT LIKES MY LESSONS SO WELL SHE WANTS ME TO BE A GUEST AT HER SUMMER HOME.

HEY! SOMEONE'S AT THE DOOR.

KNOCK KNOCK

A ROLL OF WOVEN WIRE? WHAT IN THE WORLD IS THAT FOR?

I ORDERED IT. I'M GOING TO MAKE SOME SPECIAL GUARDS FOR OUR OFFICE DOORS.

Reg. U. S. Pat. Off.: Copyright, 1949, by The Chicago Tribune.

GUARDS FOR OUR OFFICE DOORS? "PEAR-SHAPE," YOU ARE JITTERY! YOU'RE SCARED!

I'M ALSO VERY SMART, NELLIE. REMEMBER THAT.

5-15-49

REDUCING LESSONS BY MAIL, IMAGINE!

POOR AUNTIE WAS SO HEAVY.

5-16-49

IN FACT, SHE HAD BECOME ACQUAINTED WITH THE HEAD OF THAT REDUCING SCHOOL. SHE THOUGHT HE COULD BRING BACK HER HEALTH.

LESSON 12. Reduce-U- by Mail

P.S. TONE, PRES.

Reg. U. S. Pat. Off.: Copyright, 1949, by The Chicago Tribune.

THE DAY YOUR AUNT WAS ROBBED AND SLAIN, HAD SHE HAD ANY VISITORS OR COMPANY?

COME TO THINK OF IT, YES. THE MAN WHO RAN THE REDUCING SCHOOL HAD BEEN HERE.

WHY DIDN'T YOU TELL AUTHORITIES THAT BEFORE?

I-I NEVER THOUGHT OF IT, I GUESS. HE WAS JUST A FAT, LITTLE FUNNY MAN. AUNTIE WAS GREATLY AMUSED BY HIM.

CHESTER GOULD

"PEAR-SHAPE," AREN'T YOU CARRYING THINGS JUST A LITTLE TOO FAR WITH THESE STEEL WIRE GUARDS.

5-17-49

LISTEN, A BUSINESS OFFICE LIKE OURS NEEDS GUARDS ON THE WINDOWS. IT'S JUST GOOD POLICY.

Reduce-U- by Mail

20 LESSONS DOLLARS

Reg. U. S. Pat. Off.: Copyright, 1949, by The Chicago Tribune.

HOW DEEP A WATER ARE YOU IN? IS THIS PLACE A POWDER BARREL? IF IT IS, I'M LEAVING.

NOW, NELLIE!

HELLO.

CHESTER GOULD

PEAR SHAPE

ISN'T THIS JOHN CLIFFORD'S OFFICE?

NO!

BUT JOHN CLIFFORD GAVE ME **THIS** ROOM NUMBER. HE SAID THIS WAS HIS OFFICE.

LISTEN, MY FRIEND, NO JOHN CLIFFORD HAS OFFICES HERE. NOW— **GET OUT!**

BUT HE **TOLD** ME THIS WAS HIS OFFICE.

YEAH, IT'S THE SAME REDUCING COURSE AS THE ONE WE FOUND IN THE DEAD WOMAN'S ROOM! **IDENTICAL!**

THIS REDUCING COURSE IS NOTHING MORE THAN A LIST OF SETTING-UP EXERCISES. IT'S A **FRAUD.**

"P. S. TONE, PRESIDENT"

WE SUSPECT HIM OF MURDERING RICH WIDOW WALDO. OUR NEXT MOVE IS TO FIND OUT HIS "STYLE"—HOW HE OPERATES.

SAM, ARE YOU OVERWEIGHT?

OVERWEIGHT? LISTEN, I'VE GOT THE FINEST FIGURE IN MY SOCIAL SET. OVERWEIGHT, HE SAYS!

DRESSED IN WOMEN'S CLOTHES, HOWEVER, YOU WOULD **NOT** BE CONSIDERED A BETTY GRABLE.

YOU GOT ME!

HERE ARE SOME DRESSES AND SUITS, MR. TRACY. WE DIDN'T HAVE MUCH OF A SELECTION IN THE LARGER SIZES, HOWEVER.

I'LL GET THE SHOES ON WHILE YOU'RE PICKING OUT AN OUTFIT.

YOU'VE GOT TO **LOOK** LIKE AN OVER-WEIGHT MATRON —AND A **WEALTHY** ONE AT THAT.

SAM CATCHEM, THE ACTOR, I WAS KNOWN AS.

NELLIE, REMEMBER, THERE'S NO SUCH THING AS FAILURE! BE CLEVER! BE SHARP! BE LIKE ME!

NOW THE EARRINGS AND A LITTLE MORE LIPSTICK, SAM.

I'LL BE YOUR CHAUFFEUR, SAM. YOU ARE NOW GOING TO MAKE A PERSONAL CALL AT THE REDUCE-U-BY-MAIL INSTITUTE.

LET'S SEE—I HAVE SPOTS BEFORE MY EYES. I CAN'T RUN THE QUARTER MILE LIKE I USED TO. WHEN I WRESTLE, I GET PAINS IN MY BACK—

NO, DON'T TELL 'IM THAT. JUST SAY YOU'RE ANXIOUS TO LOSE WEIGHT.

NOW REMEMBER, NELLIE, WHEN ANYBODY COMES JUST PULL THE PIN AND DRAW THIS BACK—SEE? IT'S SIMPLE.

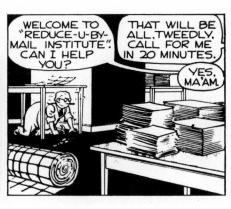

DOWN THE FIRE ESCAPE—THROUGH THE **FURNACE** ROOM, "PEAR-SHAPE" TRIES TO SHAKE OFF THE BOXER.

HE **OPENS DOORS!** HE MUST BE HUMAN!

I'D DRILL HIM BUT I'VE USED THE LAST OF MY AMMUNITION.

WHERE AM I?

UH—YEAH—I'M ALL RIGHT, TRACY. HANDCUFF HER TO ME AND GO AFTER "PEAR-SHAPE".

INTO THE BUILDING AND OUT AGAIN, IN HIS STRUGGLE TO ESCAPE THE BOXER, "PEAR-SHAPE'S" BREATHING BECOMES MORE AND MORE DIFFICULT.

IF ONLY I CAN REACH MY CAR IN THIS PARKING LOT.

WOOF WOOF

EASY, BOY! I'LL LET YOU OUT.

I WOULD HAVE HAD EVERYTHING UNDER CONTROL, BUT THAT DAME KLONKED ME ON THE **HEAD!** THEN THEY WRAPPED ME UP IN THIS WIRE.

I'LL TAKE THIS STUFF OFF FIRST.

WATCH THE GIRL, SAM. I'M GOING TO FOLLOW THE BOXER.

DOWN THE REAR STEPS AND INTO A PARKING LOT GOES "PEAR-SHAPE."

THAT DOG—HE'LL **KILL ME!** HE'LL TEAR ME APART!

I'VE **FOILED** THE BEAST! **I MADE IT!**

SLAM

USED ALL MY AMMUNITION—LOST MY **GUN!** I'M LUCKY TO GET OUT OF THERE **ALIVE.**

AS "PEAR-SHAPE" LEAVES THE PARKING LOT HE DOES NOT SEE THE BOXER LEAP TO THE ROOF OF HIS CAR.

THANK HEAVENS, I GAVE THAT MONGREL THE SLIP!

PEAR SHAPE

FOLLOW THAT CAR WITH THE DOG ON TOP!

A FEW SECONDS LATER, "PEAR-SHAPE" SUDDENLY APPLIES HIS BRAKES IN THE CONGESTED TRAFFIC.

WHAT'S THAT? HUH?

THAT DOG! THAT KILLER! WHY TH ~★★※※~!!

I'LL CUT THROUGH THE PARK—RIGHT THROUGH THE SHRUBBERY! THE LIMBS WILL SCRAPE HIM OFF THE CAR.

Reg U S Pat Off.
Copyright, 1949, by The Chicago Tribune.

OKAY, MACK! NOW WHAT DO WE DO?

INCIDENTALLY—ALTHOUGH IT HAS NOTHING TO DO WITH OUR STORY, WE OUGHT TO MENTION THAT TOMORROW IS SPARKLE PLENTY'S BIRTHDAY. SHE WILL BE 2 YEARS OLD!

5-29-49

OUR STORY OF "PEAR-SHAPE" BEING PURSUED BY DICK TRACY AND THE BOXER MUST BE SHELVED FOR ONE DAY—BECAUSE TODAY IS—MY SECOND BIRTHDAY!

5-30-49

I'M 2 YEARS OLD!

YES, SPARKLE PLENTY IS 2 YEARS OLD

Reg U S Pat Off.
The Chicago Tribune.

CHESTER GOULD

SPARKLE, YOU'RE GETTING TO BE A BIG GIRL.

WHY, SHORE! WHEN DO WE EAT THE DAD-BLAMED CAKE?

NOW, SPARKLE, IS THAT ANY WAY FOR YOU TO TALK?

OH, I MEAN THE DAD-BLAMED ICE CREAM.

WELL, THAT'S BETTER.

WHEN MUGG, THE BOXER DOG, LEAPS TO THE CAR ROOF, "PEAR-SHAPE" BECOMES DESPERATE.

HE'S STILL THERE!

SWISH

Reg. U. S. Pat Off.
Copyright, 1949, by
The Chicago Tribune.

5-31-49

RUNNING THROUGH PARK SHRUBS AND BUSHES, THE PUDGY CROOK TRIES HIS BEST TO SCRAPE THE DOG FROM THE TOP OF THE CAR.

WE'VE GOT TO FOLLOW THEM, CABBIE, PARK RULES OR NOT!

I'LL GET HIM THIS TIME!

CHESTER GOULD

DETERMINED TO STAY WITH HIS QUARRY, MUGG, THE BOXER, HANGS ON FOR DEAR LIFE—

BUT "PEAR-SHAPE" JUDGES HIS NEXT MOVE CAREFULLY. THE HUGE LIMB CATCHES THE DOG SQUARELY ON THE HEAD.

WHY THAT DIRTY ⚡★❊❋! HOLD IT, DRIVER.

THERE'S TIME ENOUGH TO GET "PEAR-SHAPE"! RIGHT NOW, MUGG'S GOT TO HAVE HELP!

DRAWING TO A SIDE STREET, "PEAR-SHAPE" ABANDONS HIS OWN CAR AND STRIKES OUT AFOOT.

--WATCH FOR BLACK SEDAN, LICENSE 1170-366-- AND SEND A CAR UP HERE RIGHT AWAY. WE'VE GOT TO TAKE MUGG TO A VET.

2-WAY WRIST RADIO

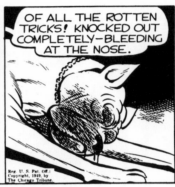

OF ALL THE ROTTEN TRICKS! KNOCKED OUT COMPLETELY—BLEEDING AT THE NOSE.

SPYING A LADY SHOPPER'S CAR CARELESSLY PARKED WITH THE MOTOR RUNNING, "PEAR-SHAPE" LEAPS INSIDE AND TAKES OFF.

SHE SAW ME DRIVE AWAY. EVERY COPPER IN TOWN WILL BE LOOKING FOR THIS CAR.

I MIGHT AS WELL FACE THE FACTS. I HAVEN'T GOT A CHANCE IN A HOT CAR.

I HEAR A SIREN NOW. I'M IN A SPOT.

EE-E-E

JUST TELL HIM HIS NEW STEAM CABINET'S HERE. WHERE DOES HE WANT IT PUT?

THE "NEW STEAM CABINET.

JUST SHOVE IT IN THAT SIDE ROOM TILL I GET AN ELECTRICIAN.

QUITE A HEALTH SPOT YOU HAVE HERE. YOU REDUCE THE FAT ONES, EH?

Jim Pistol's REST SANITARIUM Massages Specialty

I'VE GOT TO GET OUT OF HERE WITHOUT ATTRACTING ATTENTION. THAT GUY WOULD LIKE TO GET A CUSTOMER LIKE ME.

EXCUSE ME, MISTER! WELCOME TO JIM PISTOL'S REST SANITARIUM. I CAN SEE YOU NEED MY HELP.

ARRR!

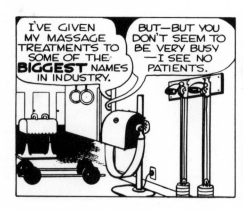

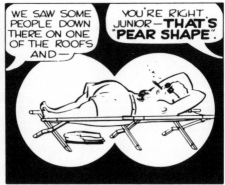

FIVE MINUTES LATER A WIRY YOUNG FELLOW IS CALLED TO A TELEPHONE.

IT'S FOR YOU, PEDRO.

—YOU TOLD ME IF I EVER NEEDED YOU, PEDRO, YOU'D DO **ANYTHING** FOR ME. WELL, THIS IS IT!

UNLESS, OF COURSE, YOU WANT ME TO "SMEAR UP" THAT NEW LIFE YOU'VE BEEN LEADING — AND I DON'T THINK YOU DO! NOW LISTEN. GET THIS CAREFULLY—

AND AT HEADQUARTERS.

WE'VE PUT A WATCH ON THE PLACE, TRACY, AND HERE'S THE DOPE—

IT'S A REST SANITARIUM AND APPARENTLY "PEAR-SHAPE" IS ONE OF THE PATIENTS.

HERE'S A LAYOUT OF THE BUILDING WE GOT FROM THE CITY INSPECTOR'S OFFICE.

LET'S SEE— THREE FLOORS AND A BASE-MENT—FRONT AND ALLEY ENTRANCE—

Reg U S Pat Off
Copyright, 1949, by The Chicago Tribune

AND BACK WITH PEDRO.

WHAT'S THE MATTER, DARLING? YOU LOOK WORRIED.

I JUST GOT A CHARTER JOB FOR THE 'COPTER THAT I DON'T WANT TO GO THROUGH WITH — H'M??

H'M?

6-12-49

THE CITY INSPECTOR SUPPLIED US WITH A FLOOR PLAN OF JIM PISTOL'S PLACE. WE CAN'T GO WRONG.

6-13-49

SAM CATCHEM AND I WILL GO INSIDE WHILE YOU MEN COVER THE EXITS.

Reg U S Pat Off
Copyright, 1949, by The Chicago Tribune.

AND AT THE CITY AIRPORT.

AT LEAST, HONEY, COULDN'T YOU TELL ME WHAT THIS CHARTER JOB **IS**! WHY IS IT SO SECRET?

NO! I **WON'T** DO IT. I'LL CALL HIM BACK AND **TELL** HIM I WON'T DO IT.

I'LL GO DOWN NOW.

CHESTER GOULD

IF YOU TURN ME DOWN, PEDRO—I'LL REVEAL YOUR PART IN THE WALDO ROB-BERY BY AN ANONYMOUS PHONE CALL TO THE POLICE. I'LL—

6-14-49

THINK IT OVER, HE SAYS. WHAT CAN A MAN THINK OVER WHEN HIS WIFE'S AND BABY'S FUTURES ARE AT STAKE?

OFFICE

Reg U S Pat Off
Copyright, 1949, by The Chicago Tribune.

HE WOULDN'T TELL US WHERE HE'S GOING—BUT DADDY ALWAYS KNOWS BEST. HE SAID HE'D BE GONE AN HOUR. WAVE BYE-BYE.

YES, I'M JIM PISTOL—OWNER AND OPERATOR. DO YOU GENTLEMEN CARE TO ENROLL IN OUR HEALTH COURSE?

PEAR SHAPE

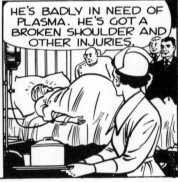

THERE IN THE DARK I SAW THOSE EYES—THE HELICOPTER HAD JUST STARTED TO LEAVE THE GROUND.

"I GRABBED THE TRICYCLE LANDING GEAR—UNDER THE FRONT OF THE MACHINE."

"I WAS ABLE TO HOLD ON BUT A FEW SECONDS—THAT'S ALL I REMEMBER."

YOUR FALL INTO THE TREE TOP KNOCKED YOU OUT. A DEAD LIMB PIERCED YOUR NECK AND YOU GOT A CRACKED SHOULDER.

WE HAVE PLENTY OF EVIDENCE THAT YOU MURDERED WIDOW WALDO, SO I IMAGINE YOU'LL BE WITH US FOR SOME TIME, "PEAR-SHAPE".

AS FOR YOU, PEDRO, THERE ARE EXTENUATING CIRCUMSTANCES—BUT YOU'LL HAVE TO EXPLAIN A LOT OF THINGS TO THE JUDGE.

TRACY, TESS IS ON THE PHONE.

286

STOOGE VILLER
1933

"MOLE"
1941

Dick Tracy's Rogues Gallery

LITTLEFACE
1941

B-B EYES
1942

PRUNEFACE
1943

MRS. PRUNEFACE
1943

THE BROW
1944

VITAMIN FLINTHEART
1944

FLATTOP SR.
1944

SHAKEY
1945

BREATHLESS MAHONEY
1946

MUMBLES
1947, 1955

SHOULDERS
1948

SKETCH PAREE
1949

Principal Characters
of the First
Twenty Years

(Arranged by the year of their initial appearance.)

1931

Ribs Mocco
Texie Garcia
Dubbs
Habeas
Big Boy
Tess Trueheart
Pat Patton
Chief Brandon

1935

Zora Arson
Chief Yellow Pony
Cutie Diamond
Mark
Bookie Joe
Toby Townley
Blake
Maybelle
Cut Famon
Muscle Famon
Bail Gordon
Bowman Basil

1936

Jim Trailer
Addie Gothorn
Lips Manlis
Athnel Jones
Nig Mahoe
Memphis Smith
Bob Honor
Mimi
Cinder Meeglio
Toyee
Kitty Manlis
Johnny Fling
Maylie

1937

Baldy Stark
Angeline
Shirtsleeve Kelton
Baldy
Madeline
Johnny Mintworth
Collie Vinsso
Danny Supeena
Mrs. Mintworth
Mable Marmer
Frank (Ankle) Redrum—
    (The Blank)

1941

Mina
Selbert
Myrna
Clara Orlin
Constable Ferret
Ginger Ferret
Trigger Doom
Czar Rennis
Joe Ballivan
Little Face Finny
Charlie Yenom
Lola
Duke
Mole
Bea Thorndike

1942

Debby
Jacques
B. B. Eyes
Clarke Van Dyke
Matri
Dianne Yollman
Amard
Tiger Lilly
Frizzletop
Cal Bullet
Clara
Pruneface

1943

Mrs. Potter
Myrtle Wreath
Nifty
88 Keyes
Mrs. Pruneface
Dr. I. O. Dyne
Needles
Laffy Smith
Miss Lure
Lt. Kirk Smith
Flattop
Nellie

1947

Misty Waters
Mel Clark
Hypo
Dahlia Dell
Bronko
Sparkle Plenty
Coffyhead
Autumn Hews
Luigi
Mumbles
Kiss Andtel

1948

Miss Varnish
Jack Will
Mrs. Volts
Brier
Acres O'Riley
Heels Beals
Big Frost
Flossie

1932

Broadway Bates
Belle
Buddy Waldorf
Alec Penn
Kenneth Grebb
Marge Dale
Steve The Tramp
Dan Mucelli
Larceny Lu
Junior

1933

Stooge Viller
Blind Hank Steele
J. Peter Twillbrain
Maxine
Old Mike
Slicer
Boss Jim Herrod
Ben Spaldoni
Confidence Dolan
Jimmy White

1934

Jean Penfield
J. Scotland Bumstead
Doc Hump
Mary Steele
Boris Arson

1938

Stud Bronzen
Lee Ting
Chief Shellbury
Tau Ming
Rottur
Noana
Ramm
Mayor Chiang
Pete Reppoc
Brighton Spotts
Jo Jo Nidle
Marro
Karpse
Halone

1939

Pop Gaines
Wolley
Scardol
Mitzi McKee
Jim Lester
Nixon
Whip Chute
Lily
Frank Rellik
Edward Nuremoh
Aunt Margot
Lola Lavir
John Lavir
Nat, The Fur King
Prof. M. Emirc
Binnie Viller

1940

Kress Kroywen
Mary X (Leola Sunny)
Mason
Rudy Seton
Junky Doolb
Jerome Trohs
Mamma
Yogee Yamma
Roloc Bard
Toirtap
Pearl Erad
Horace
Johnny Naem
Deafy
Skunk
Kitty
Krome
Lowse

1944

Vitamin Flintheart
Summer Sisters
   (May & June)
The Brow
Gravel Gertie
Snowflake Falls
Shaky

1945

Anna Enog
Measels
Paprika Gonzalez
Breathless Mahoney
Wetwash Wally
B.O. Plenty
Itchy Oliver
Kitty

1946

Diet Smith
Irma
Brilliant
Nilon Hoze
Themesong
Shoulders
Honey Dell
Christmas Early
Gargles
Influence

1949

Sam Catchem
Sleet
Twist
Pear Shape
Nellie
Talcum Freely
Spike Dyke
Sketch Paree
Mugg
Mousey

1950

Wormy Marrons
Ted Tellum
Blowtop
TV Wiggles
Bubbles Anvil

Dick Tracy's Scientific Arsenal

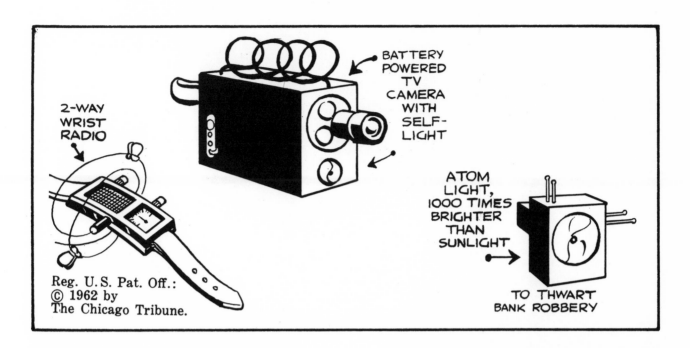